WELDING

GW00385426

A practical handbook describing the welding and cutting of metals by the oxy-acetylene and metallic arc processes

J. A. OATES, *A.M.I.P.E.*, *M.Inst.Met.*

Illustrated by

S. J. DRIVER

MODEL & ALLIED PUBLICATIONS
ARGUS BOOKS LIMITED
Argus House, St. James Road, Watford,
Hertfordshire, England.

Model and Allied Publications
Argus Books Limited
Argus House, St James Road, Watford, Herts.

© Argus Books Ltd. 1976

First Published 1955
Second Impression 1963
Third Impression 1969
Fourth Impression 1971
Fifth Impression 1973
Sixth Impression 1975
Seventh Impression 1976
Eighth Impression 1977

ISBN 0 85344 094 8

Printed by Unwin Brothers Limited, Old Woking, Surrey

CONTENTS

CHAPTER I

INTRODUCTION TO WELDING

The basic principle of welding is the same for all processes, i.e. the surfaces or edges to be joined are brought to a molten condition and the metal allowed, or caused, to intermix so that they cool to become, in effect, a single piece. The chief differences between the various processes lie in (1) the method of raising the metal to its molten condition, and (2) method by which the metal is caused to intermingle.

In forge or 'fire' welding the parts to be joined are heated in a coke fire and the metal caused to intermingle by blows from a hammer, i.e. by pressure. In the case of the various electric resistance welding processes, the surfaces to be joined are raised to the melting temperature with the aid of an electric current, and are held together under pressure so that the molten metal intermingles to form an homogeneous joint: the pressure applied to force the surfaces into intimate contact is usually referred to as the 'forging' pressure. Methods employing the above principles are known as 'pressure welding' processes.

In contrast, no forging pressure is applied during the gas and electric arc welding processes. Instead, the surfaces to be joined are merely melted and allowed to run together, i.e. intermingle. Consequently, these are known as 'fusion welding' processes.

With gas welding, the necessary heat is provided by an intensely hot flame produced by burning a mixture of oxygen and acetylene, or other combination of gases: sometimes extra molten metal is added in order to fill up the joint, the latter then consisting of a mixture of metal from the two surfaces plus the extra, or 'filler', metal.

The electric arc processes melt the surfaces by means of the heat from an arc struck between them and an electrode. The latter may comprise a piece of hard carbon (i.e. 'carbon arc welding') or, more usually, a rod of metal which melts and mixes with the molten metal of the joint surfaces (i.e. 'metallic arc welding').

During recent years there have been many important advances in both welding techniques and materials, with the result that it is now not difficult to obtain joints which are as strong as, or in some instances stronger than, the 'parent' or 'base' metal (i.e. the metal being joined).

JOINTS

As far as fusion welding is concerned there are four main types of joints (*Fig. 1*), i.e. butt, fillet, corner and edge. The butt joint (a) is employed when joining two edges together, and the (b) fillet when welding a vertical piece to a horizontal surface, securing patches and plates to other surfaces, etc. As the name implies, the corner joint (c) joins the edges of two plates, etc., at 90 degrees or any other angle. The term 'edge joint' is self explanatory (e).

In the majority of cases, filler metal is added to the joint during welding, and this necessitates the shaping or *preparation* of the edges to accommodate the extra metal. This is not required for butt joints, provided that the edges are reasonably square and smooth. The type of preparation employed (*Fig. 2*) is governed mainly by the thickness of the metal or plate involved, although the choice may also be influenced by other factors. This subject will be referred to again in later sections.

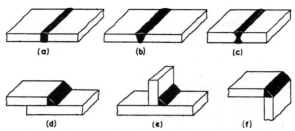

Fig. 1. The main types of joints. Key: (a) plain butt, (b) single-vee butt, (c) double-vee butt, (d) single fillet lap joint, (e) close square tee joint, and (f) corner fillet joint.

The method employed for preparing the edges will depend largely on the size of the work and the equipment available. Small work can usually be filed, chipped or ground, whilst planing or gas cutting may be necessary for larger work, or for vessels to be welded to Lloyd's Class I specifications.

In addition to preparing the edges for welding it is essential thoroughly to clean them for a distance of approximately 3 in. each side of the line of welding. It is impossible

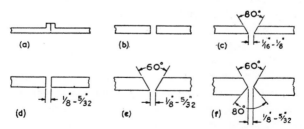

Fig. 2. Edge preparations for oxy-acetylene welding mild steel. The leftward technique should be employed for (a), (b) and (c), and the rightward for (d), (e) and (f). Key: (a) flanged, for sheet up to $\frac{1}{16}$ in. thick, (b) square edge, for $\frac{1}{16}-\frac{1}{8}$ in. thick sheet, (c) single-vee, for $\frac{1}{8}-\frac{3}{16}$ in. thick plate, (d) square edge, for $\frac{3}{16}-\frac{5}{16}$ in. thick plate, (e) single-vee, for $\frac{3}{16}-\frac{3}{8}$ in. thick plate, and (f) double-vee for plate $\frac{3}{8}$ in. thickness and over.

to make sound joints if the weld surfaces are rusty, greasy, covered with paint, etc. The reason for cleaning the surfaces 3 in. from the weld is to prevent grease or paint melted by the welding heat from running into the welding area.

Rust and paint usually can be removed by filing or grinding. Work thoroughly saturated with grease and oil (e.g. crankcases, etc.) will require careful washing in paraffin followed, possibly, by one of the degreasing treatments.

FLUXES

When heated metal is exposed to the atmosphere, it combines with the oxygen, and metallic oxides form on the surface. In the case of welds, the oxides mix with the molten metal, causing it to become porous and weak. For this reason *fluxes* are often added during welding in order to *reduce* and remove these oxides, together with any other impurities, by the formation of a fusable slag of low specific gravity. The slag absorbs the oxides, and floats on the surface of the molten metal. Some oxides are lighter, and others heavier, than the molten parent metal. For instance, in the case of mild steel the oxide is lighter, and floats to the surface without the use of a flux.

Gases are released during welding and can become trapped as the metal solidifies, thus causing *blowholes*. If a correctly balanced flux is used the gases are released before they can become trapped. The flux also increases the fluidity of the molten metal so that the possibility of blowholes is further reduced.

There is no universal flux suitable for all classes of metal, although in some instances one flux may be suitable for more than one metal.

This is due to the fact that some metallic oxides are soluble in one type of chemical but are insoluble in another. Again, the melting point of the flux must be lower than the melting point of the metal, yet not too low, otherwise the flux may be melted and driven off before completing its primary function: it will be appreciated that the melting point of different metals varies considerably.

The flux must possess the property of spreading freely over the surface of the heated metal in order to ensure complete oxide solution and absorption, yet not be too free-flowing so as to be swept from the weld area. Also, it should incorporate elements which have an affinity for oxygen, and when molten the flux should be impervious to gases which might contaminate the weld. In some cases the fluxes must include additional elements to compensate for elements lost by vaporisation or other causes during the welding operation, and so ensure the highest possible joint strength.

ACKNOWLEDGMENTS

The preparation of the following pages would have been impossible without the expert advice of two leading manufacturers of welding equipment. The author therefore gratefully acknowledges the help given by the provision of data and illustrations by The British Oxygen Co., Ltd. (gas welding and cutting) and The Quasi-Arc Co., Ltd. (metallic arc welding).

CHAPTER II

THE PREVENTION OF DISTORTION

Expansion of the heated metal, followed by contraction during cooling, often causes the work to distort. Distortion is reduced to a minimum if the parts are free to expand and contract without constraint. In the case of a lighter or a smaller part welded to a heavy part, distortion can usually be counteracted by preheating the heavy section, or by applying preheat to other areas in such a manner that the whole unit expands in the same direction as the expansion caused by the welding heat. The points of application and the amount of heat applied varies with each job, and can only be determined by experience.

In suitable cases it may be possible to reduce distortion by prebending the work in the opposite direction to that in which the welding forces will act. In all cases the amount of heat put into the weld must be kept to a minimum. Most non-ferrous metals expand more than steel.

Most distortion is caused by the heat put into the metal adjacent to the weld. Thus a hot flame (which moves quickly) will generally cause less distortion than one of lower temperature which moves more slowly and gives the heat time to travel further from the welding line.

CHILLS

Distortion may often be minimised by the use of *chills* (*Fig. 3*) to localise the heat. For example, on long straight seams in sheet and thin plate it may be possible to secure a thick piece of steel on each side of the welding line, the inner edge of each piece being bevelled to increase visibility.

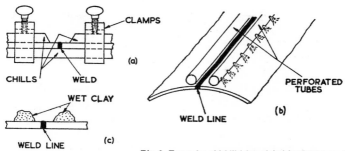

Fig. 3. Examples of 'chills' for minimising heat spread.
Key: (a) for thinner sheet, (b) for cylindrical and curved work, and (c) the use of wet clay etc.

Water jets from a perforated pipe, the jets being directed away from the weld, provide a useful solution for larger work, particularly if it has a curved surface. Wet clay or wet asbestos make useful chills which can be moulded to suit the work contours.

TACK WELDING

As welding proceeds along the seam of butt welds, the heat causes the two edges not yet welded to close together and, finally, overlap (*Fig. 4*a). To prevent this movement the edges of sheet and thinner plate are usually held firmly apart by *tack welds*, i.e. single welds spaced at regular

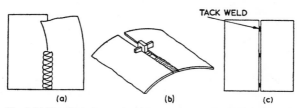

Fig. 4. (a) The effect of expansion due to welding heat, (b) a simple device to taper space the edges of long seams, and (c) the use of 'tacks' to prevent movement of the edges.

intervals along the seam (*Fig.* 4c). The size and spacing varies with the metal thickness. However, on very thin sheet, tack welding can cause considerable buckling.

Taper Spacing

On thicker plate it is customary—instead of tacking—to taper-space the two edges so that they are pulled parallel by the welding heat. The edges can be held in position by clamps, or by special wedges (*Fig.* 4b) which are moved along the gap as welding proceeds. Welding, of course, commences at the narrow end of the gap. The allowance varies with the type of material, plate thickness and speed of welding, but the following figures provide a useful guide: (1) steel—$\frac{1}{4}$ to $\frac{3}{8}$ in. per foot, (2) copper—$\frac{3}{16}$ in. per foot, (3) aluminium—$\frac{7}{8}$ in. per foot, (4) brass and bronze—$\frac{3}{16}$ in. per foot, and (5) Monel—$\frac{3}{8}$ in. per foot.

Skip Welding

Distortion can often be minimised by first welding in one direction for a short distance from the centre of the seam, and then for a short distance in the opposite direction, again starting from the centre of the seam. Then return to the end of the first portion and weld for a further short distance, repeating the above sequence until the weld is completed. This procedure (*Fig.* 5a) known as *skip welding* is very useful for long seams as it reduces the heat input.

Backstep Welding

The shrinkage forces in longer continuous seams can also be reduced by *backstep welding*, known sometimes as *stepback welding* (*Fig.* 5b). With this technique, if the general direction of welding is left-to-right, the weld is made up from

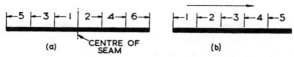

Fig. 5. Special welding sequences to reduce distortion. Key: (a) 'skip' welding and (b) 'backstep' welding.

short lengths running right-to-left. If welding is in a right-to-left direction, the runs will be from left-to-right.

PREHEATING

It is generally advisable to preheat castings prior to welding in order to (1) prevent extension of the fracture by the heat of the welding flame, (2) reduce distortion, and (3) reduce the amount of gas required for welding. Preheating is specially desirable when welding a thin part to a heavy section. A nozzle one size smaller than normal is used for welding work that has been preheated. Small work can be preheated with a blowpipe flame, but some form of furnace or oven is necessary for larger work. Types involving the use of coal or coke should be avoided.

STRESS RELIEF

This operation is concerned with removing the internal stresses caused by welding. It is only applied in cases where

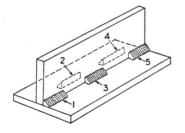

Fig. 6. Welding on alternate sides in order to reduce chances of distortion.

the stresses may deform the structure, or cause cracking of the structure or the welds. The operation merely accelerates the relief of these stresses which, as a rule, would relieve themselves over a longer period of time. On very thick plates it is advisable to stress relieve before completing the weld, i.e. after each $1\frac{1}{2}$ in. depth of weld metal is deposited.

Stress relief can be achieved in two ways, one consisting of heating the work to about 600° C. (1,100° F.) and then allowing it to cool very slowly in the furnace: this may take several days in the case of a large structure. Small parts could be heated with a torch, or gas or coke fire, and then covered with ashes, sand or slaked lime and allowed to cool slowly. It is essential to protect the work from draughts or cold air, which would accelerate the rate of cooling.

Stress relief can also be performed by 'peening', i.e. subjecting the weld to light, rapid blows from a round-nosed tool or hammer. This procedure is not as effective as heat treatment, but is particularly useful when heating facilities are not available. For general work, many welders make it a practice to peen their welds with a hammer, so improving the quality by releasing most of the stresses.

FINISHING THE WELD

As a rule, after removal of the flux residue, the only mechanical treatment required is vigorous wire-brushing to remove the surface scale from the weld. For some classes of work, however, a polished weld surface may be specified, i.e. the removal of the metal projecting above the level of the work surface. This is done by machining, grinding or polishing, generally with portable equipment.

CHAPTER III

GAS WELDING EQUIPMENT

This is a *fusion welding process* whereby the welding heat is provided by an intensely hot flame obtained by burning a mixture of gases. The more common mixtures (and their flame temperatures) are: oxy-acetylene (3,137° C.), oxy-hydrogen (2,700° C.), oxy-coal gas (2,000° C.), oxy-methane (3,000° C.), oxy-butane (3,200° C.), air-acetylene (2,325° C.), air hydrogen (2,045° C.), air-coal gas (1,800° C.) and atomic hydrogen (4,000° C.).

The oxy-hydrogen flame possesses the special advantage that it will burn in water, and for this reason is often used for underwater demolition. The coal-gas flame is very popular for cutting purposes. Methane (coke oven gas) is sometimes used in plants where this gas is available cheaply, i.e. if the plant includes coke ovens.

Flame temperature alone is not the deciding factor in choosing the gas mixture most suitable to employ. The concentration of heat possible with the flame, cost, and the ease of obtaining and transporting the gases, all influence the choice, and account for the superiority of the oxy-acetylene flame over the other industrial gases.

ACETYLENE

For welding purposes acetylene is available either compressed in cylinders (for *high-pressure welding*) or direct from a generator (for *low-pressure welding*). The pressure in a full cylinder is 225 lb. per sq. in., whilst that of generated acetylene is not much more than 0.25 lb. per sq. in. Because of this considerable pressure difference, blowpipes of different design are necessary for each process.

Acetylene is produced by the action of water on calcium carbide, as follows:

$$CaC_2 + 2H_2O = Ca(OH)_2 + C_2H_2$$

(calcium carbide) + (water) = (calcium hydroxide) + (acetylene). 1 lb. of acetylene produces 21,856 British thermal units of heat when burned, and, for complete combustion, 1 cubic foot of acetylene requires $2\frac{1}{2}$ cu. ft. of oxygen. In practice, however, approximately equal volumes of acetylene and oxygen are supplied to the blowpipe, the remainder of the oxygen being obtained from the surrounding atmosphere.

COMPRESSED ACETYLENE

Acetylene supplied compressed in cylinders is more useful than generated acetylene for small-scale use. In this condition it is quite safe to handle, is extremely pure, and is

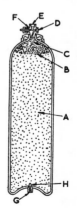

Fig. 7. Section through an acetylene cylinder. Key: (A) porous material filled with acetylene, (B) porous topping, (C) gauge filter, (D) safety plug, (E) left-hand thread, (F) valve, (G) safety plug, and (H) gauze filter.

ready for immediate use. At the top of the cylinder is an outlet valve and, as an additional precaution, a protection cap which should be replaced when the cylinder is empty: at the bottom is a safety plug. The bottom of the cylinder is flat so that it can be stood 'on end' and it should always be in this upright position whenever gas is being drawn off.

The cylinder (*Fig. 7*) is filled with a special porous material which divides the space into a number of small compartments or cells which prevent the sudden decomposition of the acetylene throughout the whole mass, should it be started accidentally by local heating. The pores are filled with acetone, in which the acetylene is dissolved under pressure. At atmospheric pressure and temperatures, the acetone dissolves about 25 times its own volume of acetylene, and at 15 atmospheres pressure this is increased to about 375 times its own volume.

The Table below gives the dimensions of cylinders in general use. It should be noted that, when fully charged, the cylinders contain about 25 per cent more than the nominal capacity.

Capacities and Dimensions of Acetylene Cylinders

Gas Capacity (cu. ft.)	Height (ft. and in.)	Diameter (in.)	Weight When Full (lb.)
60	2 — 1	$8\frac{3}{8}$	75
100	3 — $4\frac{1}{2}$	$8\frac{3}{8}$	125
200	4 — 0	$10\frac{3}{8}$	200

If the cylinders are discharged too quickly the acetylene will contain small amounts of acetone vapour, which lower the flame temperature. Also, some acetylene will remain in the cylinders and will only become available after the cylinder has been 'rested' for some time. As a guide, it may be mentioned that the discharge from a 200 cu. ft. cylinder should not exceed 25 cu. ft. per hour.

If a high rate of discharge is unavoidable, it is possible to couple two or more cylinders together (*Fig. 8*). The couplers should be obtained from a reliable manufacturer, and should not be made up from old fittings, otherwise accidents are likely to occur.

The quantity of gas withdrawn from the cylinder can be ascertained fairly accurately by weighing the cylinder before and after use on any job, and converting the difference in weight to cubic feet, on the basis of 1.1 oz. = 1 cu. ft., or 11 oz. = 10 cu. ft. Pressure gauge readings do not give a true indication of the amount of gas in the cylinder, neither

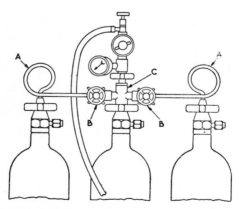

Fig. 8. The method of coupling three acetylene cylinders to meet heavy demands. Key: (A) connector pipes, (B) stop valves, (C) three-way adaptor.

do differences in pressures before and after use provide accurate means of measuring, or even estimating, the amount of gas withdrawn. This is due to the fact that the pressure increases or decreases with changes in the surrounding atmosphere. However, the weight remains unaltered, and thus provides an accurate basis for calculation.

GENERATED ACETYLENE

For the *low-pressure system*, the gas is made on site in special generators. This method is not so convenient as cylinders, but is generally preferable if large quantities of acetylene are required continuously, as when supplying a number of blowpipes.

There are two methods of generating acetylene, i.e. carbide-to-water, and water-to-carbide. The difference lies in the fact that with the first system the carbide is fed to the water, whilst the reverse procedure is employed for the latter. *Fig. 9* illustrates the Carbic generator, which is of the water-to-carbide type.

It comprises a cylindrical water tank, inside which is a conical open-end gas-bell provided with a gas-tight lid. The gas draw-off pipe passes through this lid, and the cylindrical carbide container can be withdrawn and replenished through it also. At the bottom of the bell is a sludge bucket which collects the residue of lime from the reaction.

The tank is filled to a predetermined level with water, carbide 'cakes' are inserted into the container, and the lid then clamped in position. The water rises into the gas-bell, and acts on the carbide; gas is generated and, because escape is not possible, accumulates in the top of the bell. As the action continues, the gas pressure increases to an extent sufficient to drive the level of the water in the bell down

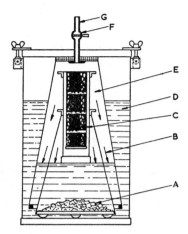

Fig. 9. The Carbic water-to-carbide acetylene generator. Key: (A) sludge bucket, (B) internal gas pressure keeping water level down, (C) carbide in container, (D) water supply, (E) gas bell, (F) gas cock, and (G) outlet pipe.

below that of the carbide, thus causing the production of gas to cease.

If the valve admitting gas to the blowpipe is now opened, the pressure of the gas in the bell is lowered and water again rises to the carbide, and the action recommenced. Thus the apparatus is entirely automatic in operation, and requires very little attention. When not in use, the gas discharge valve must be in the 'OFF' position. One pound of carbide will give 4 cu. ft. of acetylene.

As a rule, the water-to-carbide system is used for the smaller types of generators. Large plants generally employ the carbide-to-water system. For this, the carbide (in granular form) is charged into a hopper and fed by some form of conveyor to a chamber containing water, the speed of the conveyor being adjusted to suit the desired rate of gas production.

The Back Pressure Valve

As the acetylene leaves the generator it must be purified, and as much of the water vapour as possible removed. Also, before it passes to the blowpipe some form of non-return valve must be fitted into the pipe-line to deal with any back pressure from the oxygen supply cylinder, which would occur in the event of the blowpipe jet choking.

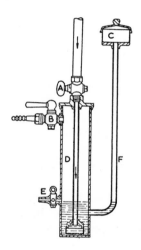

Fig. 10. The hydraulic back pressure valve. Key (A) inlet cock, (B) outlet cock, (C) filling cup, (D) water, (E) water level or overflow tap, (F) blow-off pipe.

The valve (*Fig. 10*) is a simple water seal, arranged in such a way that if the oxygen blows back along the acetylene supply tube its pressure is sufficient to drive the water out of the seal and permit escape into the atmosphere. Should this happen, the water seal must be remade before starting up again; this is done by pouring water into the filling cup until it overflows from the level tap.

Oxygen

Oxygen is supplied in cylinders painted black, and normally charged to a pressure of 120 atmospheres, i.e. approximately 1,800 lb. per sq. in. As a war-time measure, oxygen cylinders were filled to a pressure of 132 atmospheres (approximately 1,980 lb. per sq. in.) and this pressure is at present still in use. Thus a 100-ft. capacity cylinder will contain 110 cu. ft. of oxygen.

Since oxygen obeys the ordinary gas laws, the amount of gas in the cylinder is directly proportional to the pressure. For example, a 100-ft. oxygen cylinder at 120 atmospheres contains 110 cu. ft. of oxygen, and at 60 atmospheres, i.e. half the pressure, contains half the original quantity of gas, i.e. 55 cu. ft. The amount at other pressures is similarly proportional.

It should be noted that it is *extremely dangerous* to use oil or grease with any oxygen fittings. Also, it is dangerous to use oxygen in place of compressed air for any purposes. If very large quantities of oxygen are required, it is possible to couple several cylinders together.

In addition to cylinders, oxygen can also be supplied in liquid form, but this is only done in cases where the consumption is extremely high. Special equipment is necessary to store the liquid oxygen and to reduce the pressure to a figure suitable for use in the factory.

Cylinder Identification

To prevent incorrect connection, all acetylene cylinders are painted a maroon colour, and the valve outlet has a left-hand thread: the hose for connecting the blowpipe to the cylinder must be of a red colour. Oxygen cylinders are always painted black and are provided with right-hand threads. Thus it is impossible to connect an acetylene hose to an oxygen cylinder, or vice versa. The hose from the oxygen cylinder to the blowpipe must be black and provided with right-hand threads.

Cylinders for other gases are painted distinctive identification colours and in some cases bear the name of the gas on the side. In general, in order to prevent the interchange of fittings between combustible and non-combustible gases those for cylinders containing the former are screwed $\frac{5}{8}$-in. B.S.P. left-hand thread, whilst those for the latter are $\frac{5}{8}$-in. B.S.P. right-hand thread.

PRESSURE REGULATORS

The regulator provides a means of ensuring that the gas is delivered to the blowpipe at a constant, predetermined pressure, irrespective of the amount of gas in the cylinder. It is adjustable to give the pressure necessary to suit the size of blowpipe nozzle in use. Oxygen regulators are painted black and provided with right-hand hose and cylinder connections, whilst those for acetylene are painted a maroon colour and have left-hand threads.

There are two main types of regulators, i.e. single-stage and two-stage. The former comprises three elements, (1) a pressure spring, (2) a diaphragm, and (3) a valve. The pressure of the spring opens the valve, and the gas passing through acts on the diaphragm, the latter closing the valve when the gas pressure rises sufficiently to overcome the pressure of the spring. An adjustment screw enables the spring load, and hence the gas delivery pressure, to be adjusted.

The delivery pressure to the blowpipe has to be adjusted to suit the particular work in hand, and in some cases the regulator is fitted with an additional gauge for this purpose. With some regulators the pressure is indicated approximately by graduations on the pressure screw, but these indications depend to a large extent on the size of nozzle and the length of hose in service. It is mainly for this reason that the operator should adjust the flame from its appearance, rather than rely on pressure readings.

The two-stage regulator (*Fig. 11*) is a more exact instrument in which the pressure is reduced from the cylinder pressure to the working pressure in two stages. When full, an oxygen cylinder is charged to a pressure of 1,800 lb. per sq. in., and as it is used the pressure falls until it is only slightly higher than that at which the blowpipe is working. The two-stage regulator can be set to give a fixed outlet pressure which will remain constant during the whole of this period, whereas a single-stage regulator requires several adjustments to keep the flame steady.

A separate outlet valve is not usually fitted to a two-stage regulator, and if the flow of gas has to be stopped for any reason this is done by slackening the pressure screw. Since this relieves the load in the spring and the diaphragm, it prolongs the useful life of the regulator. The same precaution should be taken with either type of regulator.

It is not advisable to dismantle regulators for any reason. Once the seating of the valve is disturbed, readjustment is impossible without special tools and knowledge, and if a regulator is wrongly adjusted, it is dangerous to attempt to use it.

Several other types of regulators are also available, including one for use with cutting equipment likely to be subjected to exceptionally rough working conditions. Another type is an acetylene regulator suitable for all

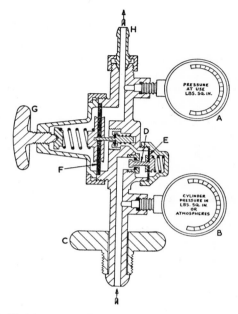

Fig. 11. A two-stage regulator. Key: (A) operating pressure gauge, (B) cylinder contents gauge, (C) connection to cylinder, (D) first-stage valve, (E) first-stage diaphragm (pre-set), (F) second-stage diaphragm, (G) pressure adjusting screw, and (H) outlet.

classes of cutting, except cast iron. Neither of these regulators is suitable for welding purposes.

PRESSURE GAUGES

The pressure gauges are fitted to the regulator, and the best types incorporate safety checks to prevent a sudden rush of gas into the gauge tube when the cylinder valve is first opened. Those for oxygen are usually graduated from o–30 lb. per sq. in., whilst acetylene gauges indicate pressures up to 15 lb. per sq. in. In the case of cylinders employed for cutting, the oxygen gauge indicates pressures up to 200 lb. per sq. in., the acetylene gauge being the same as for welding, i.e. as above. 'Cylinder content' gauges are also available. These are screwed into the neck of the cylinder and indicate pressures up to 3,000 lb. per sq. in. in the case of oxygen and 600 lb. per sq. in. for acetylene.

HOSE

Red hose must be used for acetylene and black for oxygen. As already mentioned, in order to prevent mistakes when connecting up the set, the unions are threaded left-hand and right-hand respectively. Before connecting to the blowpipe it is advisable to pass a small quantity of gas through a new hose or one which has not been used for some time in order to blow out any chalk or grit which may have settled in it.

Three sizes of rubber hose are in general use, i.e. $\frac{3}{16}$-in., $\frac{5}{16}$-in. and $\frac{3}{8}$-in. bore. The first size is used for lighter welding; $\frac{5}{16}$-in. hose is generally required with larger high-pressure blowpipes and high-pressure cutting equipment, whilst $\frac{3}{8}$-in. hose is recommended where low-pressure generated acetylene is used, and also for larger cutting blowpipes.

Hose is usually supplied in standard 10-ft. lengths, and it is convenient to attach the union nipples and nuts permanently to the ends by means of special clips, which provide an extremely neat and gas-tight connection (*Fig. 12*).

Although rubber hose is reinforced with canvas and is thus very robust and capable of withstanding high pressures, care must be taken not to damage or cut it. It can be tested for leakage under pressure by dipping in water, but it is *dangerous to test acetylene hose with any gas other than acetylene.* Do not increase the acetylene pressure for test purposes above 9 lb. per sq. in. Use only best-quality hose: inferior types tend to harden, crack and leak, and may fire internally when oxygen passes through it. Do not use unnecessarily long lengths.

Hose protectors, i.e. special non-return valves, can be fitted without any modification of the equipment. These replace the standard hose connectors to the blowpipe.

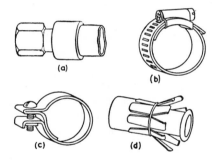

Fig. 12. Typical hose clips. Key: (a) press-formed, (b) worm drive, (c) screw-and-nut, and 'Hercules'.

BLOWPIPES

The power of a blowpipe is measured by the quantity of acetylene or fuel gas burned in an hour with a neutral flame. This is expressed in various ways, some makers defining it as the actual amount of gas (in litres) passed through the nozzle, whilst in other cases the diameter of the nozzle orifice is given. Sometimes the nozzle is merely numbered, the number denoting the thickness of plate to be welded with it.

Two important factors determine the power of the blow-pipe to be used for welding any particular thickness of metal, i.e. (1) the velocity of the gas passing through the nozzle, and (2) the quantity of gas passing through the nozzle. Both of these factors are dependent upon the pressure at which the gas arrives at the nozzle, and of the area of the nozzle orifice. The gas velocity at the moment of leaving the nozzle varies from about 200 to 600 ft. per second. A nozzle passing gas at the lower limit would give a *soft* flame, whilst a nozzle passing gas at the higher limit gives a *harsh* flame. The most satisfactory or *medium* flame is obtained when the gases have an average velocity lying somewhere between the above limits.

The blowpipe is provided with a selection of numbered nozzles to enable the power of the flame to be changed to suit different thicknesses of metal. It is also common practice to supply one long and one short neck, the use of the longer neck reducing the inconvenience from heat when welding heavy sections.

The body of the blowpipe acts as a hand grip and also contains a mixing chamber into which the two gases enter at approximately equal pressures. Some makes incorporate a device which prevents backfires or explosions. The incoming gases are controlled by two knobs or levers so positioned that they can be operated by the thumb and finger of the hand holding the blowpipe.

TYPES OF BLOWPIPES

There are two main types of blowpipes, i.e. high and low pressure, these classifications referring to the pressure at which the acetylene or fuel gas arrives at the blowpipe. They do not refer to the pressure of the gas at the nozzle. A high-pressure blowpipe *must* be used with high-pressure acetylene, i.e. from cylinders.

The low-pressure blowpipe (*Fig. 13*) is used with acetylene that comes direct from a low-pressure generator. The oxygen passes through a small nozzle into the throat of the injector where it creates a partial vacuum and mixes with the acetylene. The mixed gases give up their momentum and increase in pressure in the diverging tube of the mixer. The proportions of the injector, and the pressure at which the oxygen is supplied, have to be accurately adjusted to suit the nozzle in use, and it has not been possible to accommodate more than one size of nozzle with any one injector. Thus a separate mixer and neck pipe unit is required for each different size of nozzle.

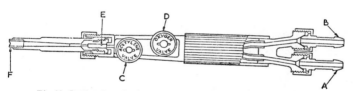

Fig. 13. Section through a low-pressure welding blowpipe. Key: (A) acetylene connection, (B) oxygen connection, (C) acetylene control, (D) oxygen control, (E) injector jet and mixing chamber, (F) interchangeable head.

Under some conditions it is possible to use an injector-type (i.e. low-pressure) blowpipe with high-pressure acetylene, *but under no circumstances should a high-pressure blowpipe be used with a low-pressure acetylene supply.*

In addition to the above types, blowpipes are also available in various sizes according to the class of work for which they are to be used, e.g. light-duty such as sheet metal, medium-duty for general work, and heavy-duty for thick plate. They differ chiefly in their weight and size, and thus,

for instance, avoid the need for holding a heavy and somewhat cumbersome blowpipe when welding thin sheet. Dual-
purpose blowpipes, so designed that they can be converted
for either welding and cutting, are also available.

Nozzle Maintenance

It is important to keep the nozzle orifice clean, but in
doing so it is important to avoid enlargement. A soft copper
wire, slightly smaller in diameter than the orifice should be
employed for this purpose. The incrustations which accumu-
late on the outside of the nozzle should also be removed
from time to time. If, in the course of time, a nozzle becomes
bell-mouthed, it can be shortened by filing about $\frac{1}{32}$ in. of
metal from the tip. Although this reduces the efficiency of
the nozzle slightly, it allows work to be continued if a
replacement is not available. If too much metal is removed,
the blowpipe will tend to backfire and, in serious cases, may
damage the blowpipe itself.

Pressure Adjustment

In practice, the correct pressure setting on the regulator
should be judged from the appearance of the flame. It is
important to adjust the pressures finally with the flame
alight, and with the control valves on the blowpipe open
about one full turn. If the blowpipe valves are only just
open, a higher pressure will be required at the regulator,
and the flame will be very liable to change if the blowpipe
receives a knock.

High-Pressure Equipment

The following equipment (see *Fig. 14*) is necessary for
high-pressure gas welding (i.e. using dissolved acetylene

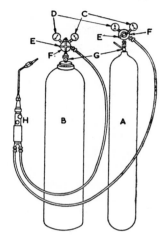

Fig. 14. A high pressure oxy-acetylene welding set. Key: (A) oxygen cylinder, (B) acetylene cylinder, (C) cylinder contents gauge. (D) outlet pressure gauge, (E) pressure regulating screw, (F) pressure regulator, (G) cylinder valve, and (H) blowpipe.

supplied from cylinders): (1) cylinder of oxygen, (2) cylinder of acetylene, (3) oxygen regulator, (4) acetylene regulator, (5) red acetylene hose and black oxygen hose, (6) blowpipe and set of interchangeable tips, (7) keys, spanners, goggles, gloves, etc., (8) rods and fluxes, and (9) a cylinder trolley (optional).

Operating Instructions

The following procedure is recommended when assembling and operating high-pressure equipment.

(1) Stand both cylinders vertically.

(2) Open the oxygen cylinder valve momentarily in order to dislodge any dirt or obstruction in the valve, and then close.

(3) Open the acetylene cylinder valve momentarily, and then close.

(4) Ensure that the jointing surfaces in the cylinder valves and regulators are free from oil or grease.

(5) Screw the oxygen regulator (painted black) into the oxygen cylinder valve.

(6) Screw the acetylene regulator (painted maroon) into the acetylene cylinder valve.

(7) Tighten the regulators in the cylinder valves. *Do not use excessive force*, but make certain that the joints are gas-tight.

(8) Connect the hose (acetylene and oxygen) to the screwed outlets of regulators. Blow gas through the hose before attaching to regulator or blowpipe, in order to remove dust or dirt, and to remove chalk when the hose is new.

(9) Connect the other end of the hose to the blowpipe, the acetylene hose to the connection marked (A), and the oxygen to the connection marked (O): keep the blowpipe control valves closed. Either a high- or low-pressure blowpipe can be used, but if a low-pressure blowpipe is employed the acetylene pressure must *never* exceed 2 lb. per sq. in. However, never use a low-pressure blowpipe with high-pressure equipment if it can possibly be avoided.

(10) Fix a nozzle of appropriate size to the blowpipe.

(11) Open the cylinder valves very slowly by means of the cylinder key. *Do not open suddenly*, or serious damage may be caused to the regulator. Open two or three full turns of the cylinder valve spindle, but not more.

(12) Set the regulators at the correct working pressures.

(13) Open the acetylene control valve on the blowpipe,

wait a few seconds until the air is blown out and pure acetylene is coming from the blowpipe nozzle, and then light.

(14) Reduce or increase the acetylene supply by means of the blowpipe valve until the flame just ceases to smoke.

(15) Turn on the oxygen by means of the blowpipe control valve until the white inner cone in the flame is sharply defined, with the merest trace of an acetylene haze. The blowpipe is now adjusted for welding steel.

On completion of the job:

(1) First turn off the acetylene by means of the blowpipe control valve, and then the oxygen.

(2) Close the cylinder valves.

(3) Open and then shut the blowpipe valves, one at a time, to release the pressure in the hose.

(4) Unscrew the pressure regulating screws on the oxygen and acetylene regulators.

FIRE PRECAUTIONS

In the event of fire in the hose or cylinder, immediately shut off the gas at the cylinder valves, or if it gets out of hand, use a wet sack or a fire extinguisher. The most prevalent cause of fires and damaged equipment is failure to shut the acetylene valve on the blowpipe completely when finishing a run of welding. If the blowpipe fires internally due to this cause, it should be placed in a bucket of water and the acetylene turned off before attempting to relight.

If, following the use of damaged equipment or the misuse

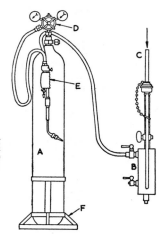

Fig. 15. A low-pressure oxy-acetylene welding set. Key: (A) oxygen cylinder, (B) back pressure valve, (C) inlet from acetylene generator, (D) oxygen pressure regulator, (E) L.P. blowpipe, and (F) stand for cylinder.

of the blowpipe, an acetylene cylinder becomes hot or fire internally, close the valve immediately and disconnect the regulator. Take the cylinder into the open air as quickly as possible, open the cylinder valve fully, and either apply water to the cylinder from a hose or, better still, immerse it in a tank of water. Should such an event occur, advise the suppliers immediately. *Never look for leaks with a light:* use soapy water.

LOW-PRESSURE EQUIPMENT

For low-pressure welding the following equipment (see *Fig. 15*) is required: (1) acetylene generator, (2) cylinder of oxygen, (3) oxygen pressure regulator, (4) hydraulic back pressure valve, (5) injector-type blowpipe and nozzles: a complete mixer and neck pipe assembly will be required for each size of nozzle, (6) black oxygen hose, and red acetylene hose; the latter is usually of larger diameter than for high-pressure equipment, (7) spanners, goggles, etc., (8) rods and fluxes, and (9) a stand for oxygen cylinder.

OPERATING INSTRUCTIONS

The following procedure is recommended when assembling and operating low-pressure equipment.

(1) Check that the generator is charged with the correct size of carbide, and correctly filled with water, in accordance with the instructions supplied by the makers. Differences exist between equipment of different makes.

(2) Check that the hydraulic back pressure valve is filled to the correct level with water.

(3) Pass a small quantity of acetylene from the generator to atmosphere to ensure that no air remains in the connecting pipes.

(4) Fit the regulator on the oxygen cylinder, and connect up the acetylene hose and the oxygen hose to the blowpipe.

(5) Fit the hose from the hydraulic valve outlet cock to the acetylene connection on the blowpipe. Attach the correct nozzle to the blowpipe.

(6) Before opening the cylinder valve, ensure that the pressure regulating screw of the oxygen regulator is screwed full out, i.e. to 'no pressure'. Then open the cylinder valve and adjust the pressure regulating screw.

The remaining stages are the same as (13) and onwards for high-pressure equipment.

When shutting down for a long period, close the oxygen cylinder valve, release the pressure screw on the regulator, and then shut the cocks (A) and (B) on the hydraulic back pressure valve.

CHAPTER IV

GAS WELDING TECHNIQUES

THE BLOWPIPE FLAME

The flame produced by burning acetylene alone is large, bushy and yellow. It produces large amounts of soot and has very little heat. As the oxygen pressure is increased a white cone begins to appear, giving two distinct parts, (1) a white inner cone and (2) the outer flame (*Fig. 16*a). The hottest part of the flame (6,000° F., i.e. 3,315° C.) is just beyond the tip of the inner cone, and provides the welding heat. The outer surrounding flame protects the molten metal from atmospheric oxidation.

THE NEUTRAL FLAME

This flame (*Fig. 16*c) is used for welding most metals, and is produced by burning approximately equal amounts of acetylene and oxygen. The inner cone is large and sharply defined, and the regulation of the flame is concerned with maintaining these two features. If these two conditions are not maintained the flame becomes either *oxidising* or *carburising*. During welding, the blowpipe tip becomes heated and this alters slightly the proportions of the two gases, usually tending to produce an oxidising flame. For this reason it is generally necessary to readjust the flame frequently whilst welding is in process.

The flame must be neither harsh nor soft, and for this reason it is important strictly to follow the maker's recommendations regarding size of the blowpipe tips and the pressure of the gases for the particular plate thickness being welded. The use of an undersize tip means that the pressure

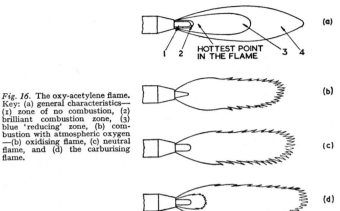

Fig. 16. The oxy-acetylene flame. Key: (a) general characteristics— (1) zone of no combustion, (2) brilliant combustion zone, (3) blue 'reducing' zone, (b) combustion with atmospheric oxygen —(b) oxidising flame, (c) neutral flame, and (d) the carburising flame.

of the gases has to be increased, this producing a harsh flame which tends to scatter the molten metal. On the other hand, if the blowpipe tip is too large the work is overheated, and to counteract this a lower gas pressure is required, resulting in a soft flame which may cause a backfire in the blowpipe.

THE OXIDISING FLAME

The oxidising flame is produced by first obtaining a neutral flame and then opening the oxygen valve slightly until the inner cone becomes shorter, although still sharply outlined (*Fig. 16*b). *This flame should never be used on steel or cast iron.*

THE CARBURISING FLAME

This flame is obtained by opening the acetylene valve slightly or, alternatively closing the oxygen valve slightly, when the blowpipe is set for a neutral flame. The flame has a long luminous outer zone, and the inner zone is ragged and indistinct in outline (*Fig. 16*d). This type of flame is used only for hard-surfacing and Stelliting operations.

PROTECTION

Certain items of protective equipment are essential in order to prevent injury to the operator. The first consists of special tinted welding goggles containing glasses of approved design. These are designed to protect the eyes from the harmful glare of the flame and the spatter of molten metal. If desired the glasses may be incorporated in a visor-type helmet which provides additional protection against flying sparks and molten metal. Gloves and gauntlets are also advisable for protecting the hands, especially when working in confined spaces.

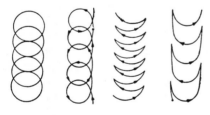

Fig. 17. Typical 'weaving' movements for the blowpipe or welding rod.

Wherever brass or other metals containing zinc are being welded, respirators must be used, because the fumes are dangerous, and a most unpleasant form of sickness can be caused by breathing them. Should this happen, the operator should immediately drink as much milk as possible. Adequate ventilation is absolutely essential when working in confined spaces, and the installation of a suction-type fan is recommended.

WELDING TECHNIQUES

As far as gas welding is concerned there are four main techniques, each of which has its own special advantages for certain classes cf work. These are as follows:

The Leftward or Forward Technique

This is performed in a forward or right-to-left direction, i.e. commencing at the right-hand end of the seam and moving to the left. The blowpipe moves forward with the flame pointing in the direction of travel, and the welding rod is held in front of the flame (*Fig. 18*). The blowpipe should be given a small sideways movement, and the rod should move steadily without sideways movement.

The filling metal should be added by a backward-and-forward piston-like movement of the rod, the rise and fall of the rod allowing forward heat to melt the bottom edges of the joint just ahead of the welding pool. The rod must *not* be held continually in contact with the molten metal, as this prevents the heat reaching the lower edges of the joint.

For steel plates above $\frac{1}{8}$-in. thickness it is customary to bevel the edges to give a Vee with an included angle of 90°. For plates above $\frac{5}{16}$-in. or $\frac{3}{8}$-in. thickness, two or more passes are required. When welding plates above $\frac{1}{4}$-in. thick

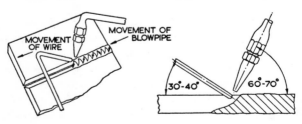

Fig. 18. The leftward welding technique.

it is rather difficult to obtain thorough fusion at the bottom of the Vee, and to ensure uniform penetration. For this reason it is considered that the maximum economical thickness limit of leftward welding on steel is $\frac{3}{16}$ in.

Rightward or Backward Welding

With this technique welding is performed from left to right. The flame is directed towards the completed weld.

The blowpipe is *not* given any sideways movement, and the welding rod has a roughly circular movement which is a combination of a transversal movement across the weld and a lateral movement along the centre line of the weld (*Fig. 19*). The movement must be uniform and should never reach the bottom of the weld. The end of the rod should be parallel to the sloping face of the deposited metal.

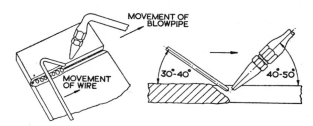

Fig. 19. The rightward welding technique.

Although of principal use for making horizontal or downhand welds, the technique can also be applied to vertical and overhead welding: it is also advantageous for butt and fillet welds in steel pipes, and for fillet welds in steel plate or sections.

With rightward welding it is possible to increase the 'no bevel' limit to $\frac{5}{16}$ in. For plates over $\frac{5}{16}$-in. thickness a 60°

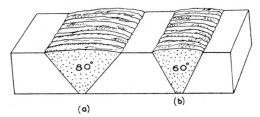

Fig. 20. Illustrating the economy of weld metal achieved by the rightward technique. Key: (a) leftward weld and (b) rightward weld.

Vee is necessary (*Fig. 20*). The blowpipe nozzle must be larger than for leftward welding in order to exercise control over the weld metal: this increases the welding speed.

Vertical Upward Welding

By arranging the welding seam in the vertical plane, steel plates from $\frac{1}{16}$ to $\frac{5}{8}$ in. thick can be welded without bevelling the edges. For thicknesses up to $\frac{3}{16}$ in. this method of welding may be carried out by one welder working from one side of the seam (*Fig. 21*); above $\frac{3}{16}$-in. thickness, two welders are employed, working simultaneously on opposite sides of the

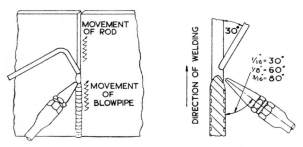

Fig. 21. Single-operator vertical welding.

seam (*Fig. 22*). The welding is started at the bottom of the
seam and carried out in an upward direction.

While the angles of the blowpipes and welding rods for
the two-welder technique are constant for all thicknesses,
the blowpipe angle for the single-welder technique varies
according to the plate thickness. Up to $\frac{1}{8}$-in. thickness the
blowpipe has only one movement, i.e. forward along the
seam, but as the thickness increases, a small circular motion
is imparted to the end of the luminous cone in order to
maintain both plate edges in a state of equal fusion.

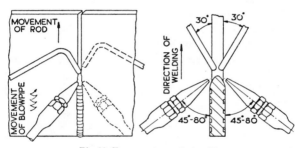

Fig. 22. Two-operator vertical welding.

When starting a weld, first heat the edges sufficiently to
fuse them through for their full depth, producing a small
round hole between the edges: this hole must be maintained as welding proceeds. The technique is really one of
'forward' welding, the welding rod being fed into the weld
puddle in front of the blowpipe, preceding the blowpipe
along the seam. In the case of the two-welder technique, it
is very important to hold both blowpipes at equal angles,
and for both operators to weld at the same point. Both
flames should be 'matched' before starting to weld.

The Lindewelding Technique

This is a butt welding technique (*Fig. 23*) for *steel* which, although particularly suitable for pipe welding, is equally applicable to ordinary flat underhand butt seams on steel plates. The operation is performed with normal blowpipes and equipment, but a special silicon-manganese rod should be used instead of low-carbon steel types.

The important difference between the Lindewelding process and others is the employment of an excess-acetylene flame, by which the surface to be welded is heated and carburised so that the melting point of the surface film is considerably lower than that of the normal base metal. As this carburised film melts, the oxide skin is fluxed off so that weld metal from the welding rod may be rapidly added. Fusion between the base metal and the weld metal results without the necessity of deep coating the base metal surfaces. When viewed through welding goggles the melting

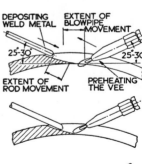

Fig. 23. The Lindewelding technique.

of the metal skin has the appearance of a 'sweating' or 'wet' surface.

Lindewelding is most suitable for steel thicknesses above $\frac{1}{4}$ in. and thus the edges should always be bevelled to an included Vee of not less than 70°. If desired, the edges may be kept in alignment by tacking at intervals of 9 to 12 in., according to the plate thickness.

The length of the excess acetylene flame should be $1\frac{1}{8}$ to 2 times the length of the inner or normally neutral cone. The flame has the important function of 'wetting' the base metal adjacent to, and ahead of, the welding puddle for a short distance, and to prepare it for fusion with added weld metal. Too large a welding flame will produce hard brittle welds, while if the flame is too small the 'wetting' action will decrease or even vanish completely.

The manipulation for Lindewelding is comparatively simple. The flame and rod are directed towards each other in the plane of the joint, the angle between them being about 120°. The flame should be directed alternately on the Vee and on the rod, in a direction parallel to the line of welding: the flame heat is directed mainly on to the welding rod.

The rod motion is normally 'push and pull', in which the molten metal is flowed to the bottom of the Vee after it has been properly prepared for fusion. The relative motions of the rod and flame are alternately towards and away from each other, these movements of rod and flame being in the line of the weld. When the Vee is wide, a slight oval movement may be combined with the straight-line movement of flame and rod.

It is very important not to push weld metal ahead on to base metal that is not sweated, as fusion is not obtained and blowholes and adhesion may result. If it is difficult to 'wet' the base metal properly, the flame should be played on the metal sufficiently to start melting or breaking down of the edges. The inner cone should *never* touch either the welding rod or the surface of molten metal at any time.

CHAPTER V

GAS WELDING VARIOUS METALS

WELDING CAST IRONS

The flame should be neutral, and applied at an angle of $60°$ to $70°$ to the surface (*Fig. 24*a). The weld should consist of a series of overlapping pools, and the rod allowed to fall naturally into the weld, stirring or puddling as required. The inner cone must not come into contact with the weld metal, otherwise the metal will absorb carbon and become hard and brittle. It is desirable to preheat cast iron to a dull red colour in order to avoid temperature stresses, and after completion the casting should be allowed to cool slowly.

A flux is necessary to prevent oxidation, and the prepared edges (*Fig. 24*b) should be thoroughly cleaned. The welding rods must be of good quality. The powdered flux should be applied to the heated rod, to which it will adhere, and from which it will be transferred to the prepared surface.

After completion of the weld it is easier to remove the oxide and the flux by means of an old file before the casting is cooled; final cleaning up by filing and grinding when cold.

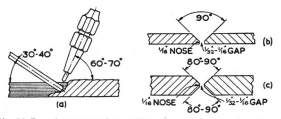

Fig. 24. Data for oxy-acetylene welding of cast iron. Key: (a) rod and blowpipe angles, (b) single-vee preparation for thicknesses up to $\frac{1}{2}$ in. and (c) double-vee preparation for greater thicknesses.

Malleable Iron

Malleable iron cannot be flame welded. One type can, however, be bronze-welded.

Mild Steel

This material can be welded without difficulty. *All procedures described throughout this book refer to mild steel unless stated otherwise*. Flux is not necessary because the oxide is lighter than the molten metal, and floats to the surface.

Alloy Steels

In general, the welding of these steels follows that for mild steel, except that preheating is generally advisable. Suitable welding rods must be used in order to ensure that the mechanical properties of the joint are the same as those of the parent metal.

Carbon Steels

The general welding procedure follows that for mild steel. To avoid cracking, and to ensure soft weld metal, preheating to about 400° C. is desirable in the case of high-carbon steels. Slow cooling is essential, otherwise the steel will be hard and brittle. The use of good-quality rods is important.

Stainless Steel (Nickel Chrome Alloys)

Although the 12 to 14 per cent chromium group can be welded, the advice of the maker of the steel must be sought before commencing to do so: in addition to the use of special filler rods, heat treatment may be necessary to prevent cracking and to maintain the corrosion-resistance properties of both weld and parent metal. The 18/8 variety can be welded without difficulty, provided that the correct procedure is adopted.

The use of a rod containing columbium facilitates the welding of stainless steel. Although some authorities suggest that a flux is not necessary, it *should* be used because it helps to promote fluidity and a smooth bead of penetration, and reduces the possibility of oxide inclusions. It should be mixed to a paste and painted on the *underside* of the sheet. The welding rod should also be fluxed by heating and dipping in the flux, which forms a varnish over the end.

Thin sheet should be welded with a rod of diameter equal to the sheet thickness. Rods slightly smaller in diameter than the thickness are used for thicker sheets.

It is desirable to use a nozzle one or two sizes smaller than for an equivalent thickness of mild steel, and a flame that is neutral. To ensure complete absence of oxidising conditions, it is better to have the slightest trace of excess of acetylene haze in the flame, since too much oxygen will result in porous welds: too much acetylene will give brittle welds having a milky appearance after polishing. Edge preparation is similar to that for mild steel, except that flanging of thin sheet is not usually possible.

The leftward or forward method of welding may be employed, using a somewhat steeper blowpipe and rod angles than for mild steel. The angles between the plate and the nozzle, and the plate and the welding rod respectively, should be 70° to 80°. The inner cone should impinge on the molten pool. The welding rod should remain in the outer flame envelope in order to avoid oxidation by contact with the atmosphere.

The flux must be mixed with water in a non-metallic

container, and only a flux made specially for stainless steel welding should be employed.

To avoid oxide inclusions, the molten metal must be agitated as little as possible, and the feed rod kept in the pool and not allowed to drop into the weld. To ensure complete penetration, the blowpipe is given slightly more lateral movement, so as to increase the size of the pool of molten metal. Scale and oxide must be removed from the finished weld by grinding, polishing, or the use of a descaling solution.

ALUMINIUM CASTINGS

The greatest enemies to successful aluminium welding are oil and grease. Thus the casting must first be thoroughly degreased. If this is not possible, bevel the edges to an included angle of 80° to 90° and clean them with a wire brush. The surface on both sides of the Vee should be filed or wire-brushed clean to a width of approximately 1 inch.

Aluminium castings *must* be preheated. It is very easy to overheat the casting, causing it to collapse under its own weight and be ruined, and for this reason it should be carefully supported so that it cannot sag. The correct preheat temperature will be indicated by the charring of sawdust or the melting of a piece of 50 per cent tin: 50 per cent zinc solder. The casting must be shielded by sheet metal to prevent the preheating flames from coming into direct contact with it.

The blowpipe flame adjustment is neutral with a very slight haze of excess acetylene in order to ensure a non-oxidising flame. The flame should be very soft, and for preheated castings a nozzle one or two sizes smaller than for cold welding is desirable.

The speed of welding increases towards the end of the run. The flame must be maintained steadily over the weld, and not moved up and down. Any tendency to partial collapse or excessive penetration should be rectified by instantly lifting the flame well clear, and not by gradually withdrawing the flame, as this will only make matters worse.

The welding rod must be fused in the flame, and after it is deposited in the Vee the molten metal is worked with the end of the rod, when necessary, to bring oxide to the surface and ensure penetration to the bottom of the bevel. Flux *must* be used, and all traces subsequently removed in order to prevent corrosion. After completion of welding, the casting must be allowed to cool slowly and uniformly.

SHEET ALUMINIUM

Preparation of the edges of sheet aluminium is similar to that for other non-ferrous metals. It is usually quite sufficient to clean them with a wire brush, file, or suitable abrasive stone. Sheet up to $\frac{1}{8}$ in. thickness should be butt welded without bevelling, whilst for greater thicknesses bevelling to an included angle of 80° to 90° is advisable.

Tacking is often necessary in order to maintain the edges in correct alignment before welding. The correct taper allowance, if tacking is not employed, is $\frac{3}{16}$ in. per foot run.

No welding rod is required for flanged edges of 20-gauge thickness and less. For thicknesses up to $\frac{3}{8}$ in. the diameter of the rod should be $1\frac{1}{2}$ to 2 times the thickness of the sheet although, in practice, rods greater than $\frac{1}{4}$-in. diameter and smaller than $\frac{3}{32}$ in. are rarely used.

Types of joints should be avoided which are likely to trap flux that cannot subsequently be removed. When tube assemblies are welded it is desirable to drill holes to enable

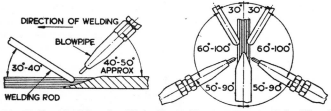

Fig. 25. Data for leftward welding of thin sheet aluminium.

Fig. 26. The two-operator upward welding of thick aluminium sheet.

the flux to be completely cleared, and in order to avoid subsequent corrosion of the metal the butt joint should be used rather than the flanged type.

On sheet up to $\frac{3}{16}$ to $\frac{1}{4}$ in. the best technique is the leftward or forward method. The angles of the rod and the blowpipe are shown in *Fig. 25*: the angle of the blowpipe decreases to 25° to 30° as welding proceeds. For thickness above $\frac{1}{4}$ in. the two-operator vertical method should be adopted wherever possible (*Fig. 26*).

DURALUMIN AND ALCLAD

Gas welding is not recommended for these metals because (*a*) the weld metal has a much lower strength than the parent metal and (*b*) there is a tendency for cracking in the weld area. In cases where strength is not important, a 5 per cent silicon rod could be employed, following the general technique given above for welding aluminium alloys. The electrical spot welding process provides the most satisfactory method of joining sheet.

COPPER

Only the *deoxidised* type of copper can be fusion welded; the other grades are not suitable. Whilst it is possible to weld small pieces of copper plate without a flux, flux is usually necessary for longer seams. The principal constituent of copper fluxes is borax, but to obtain the best results it should be compounded with certain other chemicals, and for this reason one of the proprietary brands should be used.

Butt welds in plates should be set with a gap which diverges by about $\frac{3}{16}$ in. per foot, and a backing strip covered with dry asbestos will provide support and concentrate the heat: it is essential to dry the asbestos, because steam causes porosity.

The edges should be cleaned and coated with flux on *both* sides, and flux should be painted on the welding rod. A rod thinner than 14 S.W.G. should not be used, and it is desirable to select a thicker rod than would be used for an equivalent thickness of steel.

The flame should be neutral, and to ensure this, it should be adjusted to show a trace of excess acetylene feather. To reduce heat losses the blowpipe is held fairly steeply, the lateral movement being confined to the seam: for the leftward technique, the inner cone of the flame should be maintained at about $\frac{3}{8}$ in. from the metal, using the angles shown in *Fig. 27*. Copper roofing in 22 to 24 S.W.G. sheet is often flanged to a height of 2 to $2\frac{1}{2}$ times the thickness and welded without feed rod.

Welds in thin plate should be completed in one run, although this will not be possible for thicker plate. Where possible, the vertical upward method, however, is to be preferred, and plates over $\frac{1}{8}$ in. thick can be welded by this procedure. Light hammering at temperatures above 600°, followed by cold hammering, increases the mechanical properties.

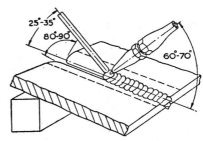

Fig. 27. The leftward welding of copper.

Care must be taken to avoid contamination of deoxidised copper with oxygen when heating the metal. *Copper should not be tack welded.* To avoid cracking, long seams can be started one-third of the total length from one end, carrying the weld to the end in one operation, and then returning to the starting point to complete the remainder.

BRASS

The chief difficulty in welding brass is the volatilisation or loss of zinc due to the fact that the melting point of zinc is lower than that of brass. This is indicated by heavy fumes and a white deposit upon the surface of the work around the weld. The loss of zinc causes blowholes or porosity in the weld, resulting in reduced strength and a pitted appearance when the weld is polished.

The 'boiling' of the molten metal and loss of zinc can be prevented by using an oxidising flame, which forms a skin of zinc oxide on the surface of the molten metal, thus preventing evaporation of the molten zinc. A soft flame is desirable, so do not increase the oxygen pressure. To compensate for the loss of heat due to the reduction in acetylene, it is advisable to use a larger-size nozzle than normally employed for other metals of the same thickness. Do not reduce the acetylene more than is necessary to prevent fuming, otherwise the molten metal will be very sticky and difficult to manipulate.

The exact amount of reduction of acetylene or excess oxygen varies according to the zinc content of the brass, and is best determined by making a molten puddle on a scrap piece of the metal to be welded. Start the test with the flame only slightly oxidising and notice the fumes, wearing goggles for this; then gradually reduce the acetylene until fuming ceases. Now make a test weld and examine it for blowholes; if they are still present make further tests with a greater excess of oxygen, until no blowholes are visible in the weld.

BRONZES

In bronzes having relatively large amounts of tin and lead, e.g. phosphor bronze or gunmetal, 'boiling' starts when the metal has reached about a red heat. This indicates that a *neutral flame* must be used for both preheating and welding.

Alloys that have a large amount of lead (5 per cent or more) may give trouble because of excessive formation of lead oxide; this difficulty can be overcome by an abundant use of flux applied as a paste to the welding rod. The *reducing* portion of the flame should be used for welding, i.e. the blue cone should be held approximately 1½ to 2 in. clear of the molten metal.

Bronzes containing fairly high percentages of nickel are whitish in colour, and are known as silver or nickel bronzes. These should be welded with *slightly oxidising flame*: this applies also to manganese bronzes.

Mix the flux to paste, and paint on the *top and underside* of the edges, and on the welding rod. Alternatively, flux can be applied by dipping both the plates and the welding rod in water, and sprinkling on the flux *before* welding.

Preheat the metal to a dark red colour (with the blowpipe) before commencing to weld. Hold the cone of the flame fairly close to the surface of the weld. Maintain the welding rod in the molten puddle, and do not lift rod or blowpipe until the weld is finished.

Confine the heat to the narrowest possible zone by placing carbon blocks, asbestos, firebricks or copper chill bars on each side of the weld, both on the top and undersides of brass sheet. It may be necessary to use a slightly larger flame if copper chill bars are used, in order to counteract the extra heat absorption. On long seams, the welding rate should be increased as the weld progresses and the metal becomes hotter. In order to obtain a weld which matches in colour the metal being welded, use a welding rod of similar composition, together with a bronze welding flux.

Magnesium Alloys

The surfaces to be welded must have all the surface protection coating thoroughly removed and, in the case of castings, degreasing is absolutely essential. Magnesium oxidises rapidly when heated, and will ignite if overheated, and should this happen the fire should be extinguished by sand, *not water*. A neutral or slightly reducing flame is essential: an oxidising flame will burn the metal. Flux tends to prevent firing, and should be painted on the *bottom as well as the top* of the weld: paste is made by mixing small quantities, as required, with alcohol or methylated spirits.

Sheets should be first tacked, and the ends then completely welded for a distance of about 2 in., any warping being removed by dressing with a wooden mallet while hot. The tacks should be refluxed before completing the entire seam.

The edge preparation is the same as for aluminium, but a nozzle one size smaller than for aluminium can be used. The leftward technique should be employed, with a blowpipe angle of about 30° to the plate, so as to run the molten flux ahead of the weld. The weld should be built up above the general level, and the excess machined off: on *no account* should it be hammered down. Castings should be preheated to about 300° C.

HARD FACING

Hard facing is a process for depositing a hard wear-resistant or tough surface on a softer metal. It can be performed either by the oxy-acetylene flame or by the electric arc. One of the best known is the Stellite process, which consists of depositing one of the proprietary 'Stellite' alloys, available in a number of grades of hardness and toughness. The method described below is a non-fusion or braze-welding process possessing the advantage that, because the two metals are not fused together in the generally accepted sense, the composition of the alloy remains unaltered. Stellite can be applied to nearly all irons and steels, including the 18/8 austenitic stainless group, but not to non-ferrous metals.

When facing steel, the surface should first be cleaned by grinding, machining, chipping or filing, and all sharp corners or edges removed. Preheating to a red/black heat (400° to 500° C.) prevents cracks forming in the deposited metal. Small parts may be preheated by the oxy-acetylene flame, but if the part is large it will be necessary to heat in a furnace. When preheating with the blowpipe, the flame should be adjusted to *neutral*. After completion of facing, *slow cooling is essential:* cooling can be retarded by immersing the part in lime or mica dust.

The correct facing flame contains an excess of acetylene. The size of the blowpipe nozzle depends upon the thickness of material to be faced, but a size should be selected that gives a soft flame. As a further assurance that a soft flame is produced, it is recommended that standard pressures of both gases for the nozzle used be reduced by 20 per cent.

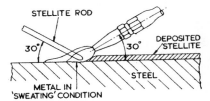

Fig 28. Data for the Stellite hard-facing process.

After general preheating with the neutral flame, the flame is adjusted to the facing conditions, i.e. with excess acetylene. The surface is then further preheated until the spot where it is desired to commence depositing begins to 'sweat', i.e. through the welding goggles it appears wet. While doing this, the end of the Stellite rod is also preheated in the flame. When the sweating condition is reached, the end of the rod is brought in line with the white cone, and the rod melted on to the surface. If the steel is at the correct sweating heat and the flame properly adjusted, the Stellite will flow and spread like solder on a tinned surface. It must be allowed to flow of itself and not forced to spread by being puddled with the rod.

The desired thickness of coating should be built up in one operation. It is usually not necessary to deposit thicknesses greater than $\frac{1}{8}$ in. At the finish of the deposit, withdraw the flame gradually, allowing the Stellite to solidify slowly in the flame. The blowpipe and rod angles are shown in *Fig. 28*.

CHAPTER VI

FLAME CUTTING METHODS

The cutting of iron and steel by the oxygen process merely involves the direction of a closely regulated jet of pure oxygen on to an area previously heated to ignition temperature (bright cherry-red colour) and, as the iron is oxidised, uniformly moving the oxygen jet so that a narrow cut or 'kerf' is formed. Since only the metal within the direct path of the oxygen jet is acted upon, very accurate results can be obtained if close control is exercised.

The cutting blowpipe (*Fig. 29*) comprises (1) a central nozzle supplying the cutting jet of oxygen surrounded by (2) an annulus through which passes the fuel gases for preheating. Both are fed from separate gas supplies and have separate control valves. The fuel gases most widely employed are acetylene, coal gas, propane and hydrogen, and it is essential to use a cutting blowpipe and nozzle designed specially for the particular gas being used (*Fig. 30*).

For hand cutting, first set the preheating flame to neutral and rest the blowpipe on its guide (*Fig. 31*) so that the white cone is $\frac{1}{4}$ in. from the work surface. When the metal reaches

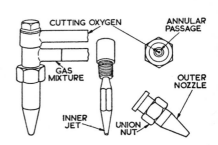

Fig. 29. Details of the oxy-acetylene cutting jet.

56

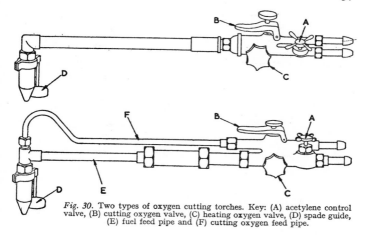

Fig. 30. Two types of oxygen cutting torches. Key: (A) acetylene control valve, (B) cutting oxygen valve, (C) heating oxygen valve, (D) spade guide, (E) fuel feed pipe and (F) cutting oxygen feed pipe.

a bright red colour, move the valve to switch on the oxygen cutting supply. In the case of steel above 8-in. thickness or cast iron above 3-in. thickness it is advisable to use an oxygen regulator capable of passing larger volumes of oxygen than for welding, and to cut with a special blowpipe having larger gas passages.

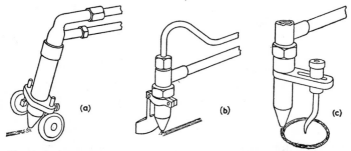

Fig. 31. Cutting torch accessories. Key: (a) wheels to facilitate straight cutting, (b) spade guide to control the nozzle height, and (c) a circle cutting attachment.

Move the cutter steadily at a speed which produces a smooth cut. Keep the white cone just clear of the work surface, and ensure that the cut has penetrated before commencing to move the cutter. Whenever possible, the operator should draw the cutter towards him.

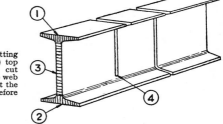

Fig. 32. Sequence for cutting through a girder. This is (1) top flange, (2) turn over and cut bottom flange and (3) cut the web last. Metal will be splashed at the radii (4) if the web is cut before the bottom flange.

The edge of thick plate should be well heated before commencing to cut. When cutting round bar a nick should be made with a chisel at the point where the cut is to start: this makes it much easier to start the cut. When starting a cut away from the edge first either drill a hole, or pierce a hole with the cutter. All oxide and scale should be removed from the line of cut prior to commencing.

CUTTING CAST IRON

Compared with mild steel, the quality of accuracy and finish is poor. A special blowpipe is necessary for cutting cast iron. It has larger passages to pass greater quantities of both oxygen and acetylene. Cast iron cutting requires an excess of acetylene in the heating flame, and for this reason dissolved (cylinder) acetylene should be used, because generated acetylene will not supply sufficient fuel gas.

Hold the blowpipe so that the end of the nozzle (not the excess cone) lies $\frac{5}{16}$ to $\frac{1}{2}$ in. above the surface; give the nozzle a swinging motion (*Fig. 33*), describing semi-circles over the end of the line of cutting, and heat a semi-circular area about $\frac{1}{2}$ to $\frac{3}{4}$ in. diameter to a bright cherry-red. Move the nozzle just off the heated edge, open the cutting valve quickly and move the cutter forward along the line of the cut with the same swinging motion. The width of the swings should be about $\frac{1}{2}$ in.

During the progress of the cut the motions are roughly as follows: Advance the nozzle about $\frac{1}{2}$ in. to burn off the molten surface, then quickly move it backward to burn through the comparatively dark layer and lower section; then hold it steady for a moment to heat the upper surface. Continue moving the nozzle in this manner at the rate of about one complete circle per second.

These directions apply to the cutting of good-quality grey cast iron. In cutting poor-quality iron, follow the same directions, but instead of using the motion of the blowpipe described above, advance the nozzle slowly, describing $\frac{1}{4}$ to $\frac{1}{2}$ in. wide semi-circles across the line of the cut, holding the blowpipe at an angle of about 75°, pointing backwards.

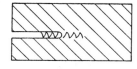

Fig. 33. Blowpipe manipulation when cutting cast iron.

STACK CUTTING

This is the technique of flame cutting a number of identical parts simultaneously from a 'stack' or pile of thin plates clamped tightly together.

In general, for plate of moderate thickness it has been found that the best results are obtained on a stack of about 3- to 4-in. thickness, although stacks of greater thickness can readily be cut. After 4-in. thickness is exceeded, the accuracy diminishes somewhat due to the greater difficulty in effecting tight clamping. On the other hand, a small stack is generally used when cutting light-gauge metal so as to prevent melting the top sheet edge with the large pre-heating flame which it would be necessary to use for a thicker stack. Clean plates, and the removal of trapped air from between the sheets, is essential for good results.

Flame Gouging

This is a method of quickly and accurately removing a narrow strip of surface metal, but differs from other flame cutting processes in that the cutting action does not progress all the way through the thickness of the metal. A special nozzle is necessary to deliver a relatively large volume of oxygen at low jet velocity which, coupled with proper pre-heat flame distribution and correct manipulation of the gouging blowpipe, will cut a smooth, accurately defined groove. By using nozzles of different sizes and by varying angle, the groove can be made to any width and depth.

The Oxygen Lance

It is sometimes necessary to cut away really massive sections of steel that are too big for the largest blowpipe. In such cases use is made of the *oxygen lance*. The cut is started by heating the work at one spot and passing a stream of oxygen to it via a long steel tube, which may be up to 15 ft. long. The tube is screwed into a special holder, coupled by hose to oxygen cylinders. As the cut proceeds the tube or 'lance' burns away.

CHAPTER VII

TYPES OF ELECTRIC ARC WELDING

Electric arc welding is a fusion process in which electric energy is employed to produce the heat (i.e. the arc) necessary to effect fusion. An electric arc is nothing more than a sustained spark between two terminals which, in this case, are the work and the electrode. The instant that the arc is formed, the temperature at the point of welding rises to approximately 6,500° F., this tremendous heat being concentrated at the point of welding which is, also, the end of the electrode. It melts a small pool of metal in the work and, in the case of metallic arc welding, also melts the end of the electrode, which feeds into the pool and thus provides additional metal.

CARBON ARC WELDING

There are three common types of electric arc welding, viz. carbon arc, metallic arc, and Helium arc welding. In the case of carbon arc welding the arc is formed between the work and the end of a carbon rod held in a holder. The heat of the arc melts a small pool in the surface of the work, and this is kept molten by playing the arc across it. If required, extra metal is added by means of a filler rod. This process is not suitable for vertical or overhead welding. The carbon electrode is usually joined to the negative pole of the current supply and the work is connected to the positive. This ensures that carbon particles are not carried over in the flame into the weld, as this would cause a brittle joint.

To weld, the work is touched with the end of the carbon (held in a holder), which is then immediately withdrawn slightly, causing an arc to form between the end of the carbon and the work. The length of the arc can be varied by holding the end of the carbon closer to, or further from, the work, and it is a matter of experience to determine the optimum length of arc which provides the correct heat for the particular conditions and type of work involved. It is important to maintain a steady gap so that the arc burns cleanly without spluttering.

However, the carbon-arc process is not now very widely employed, its use being largely reserved for such purposes as welding copper, galvanised steel, and cast iron. It also provides an economical means of cutting in cases where a smooth surface is unnecessary.

ARGON ARC WELDING

This process uses a single tungsten electrode which is provided solely for the purpose of producing and sustaining an arc, and not to furnish filler metal, i.e. it does not melt. If extra metal is required, it is added from a separate filler rod which is fed into the arc in the normal manner.

The arc, filler metal, and molten pool are protected from the atmosphere by a shield of *inert* argon gas supplied through an annular opening in an electrically-insulated tube surrounding the electrode (see *Fig. 34*). In America, helium gas is cheaper and thus is used instead of argon, the process being known as 'heliarc' welding. The general principles are, however, the same in both cases. Both hand-operated and automatic equipment are available.

To obtain the best results, direct current (with the electrode positive) is employed. It is essential to hold a constant arc length and also, as in gas welding, to manipulate the filler rod in the correct manner. With some types of joints, of course, the use of a filler rod is not necessary.

The special value of this process lies in the fact that argon and helium are 'inert' gases, and thus if the molten metal is protected by a blanket of these gases, corrosion due to combination with atmospheric oxygen will not occur. Also, the use of a flux is unnecessary because of the complete absence of air, and thus much better weld properties are obtained. For these reasons the argon arc process provides an ideal method of welding certain metals which are very difficult to weld by other means, e.g. aluminium and its alloys, copper and its alloys, stainless steel and magnesium.

In most cases welding can be carried out with the types of power plant used for ordinary metallic arc welding, although a special torch is, of course, necessary. However, for certain types of work additional equipment such as series capacitators and ionisers are essential.

Metallic Arc Welding

Of the various methods of arc welding, the metallic process is undoubtedly the most common and, for general purposes, the most convenient. The arc is struck between the work and the end of a metallic wire or rod, and under the intense heat of the arc a small part of the work is brought to the melting point almost instantaneously. The other end of the arc, i.e. the tip of the metallic wire, is also melted and tiny globules of molten metal form and are forced across the arc and deposited in the molten pool. These globules are actually *forced across the arc* and do not drop by gravity, except when the work is flat. It is this fact that enables the use of metallic arc welding in overhead positions. It will be appreciated that were it not for this feature the metal would fall downwards when welding in overhead positions.

CHAPTER VIII

EQUIPMENT FOR METALLIC ARC WELDING

Electricity from the mains is usually at too high a pressure (or voltage) for arc welding. Hence the pressure of alternating current (A.C.) mains is reduced to 70/100 volts by means of a static transformer, and that of direct current (D.C.) mains to 55/70 volts by means of a motor generator set. Welding current may also be supplied by generators belt-driven from line shafting or directly coupled to a petrol or diesel engine. The engine-driven sets are self-contained units which are often mounted on a trailer for easy portability. Incorporated in, or supplied with, the transformer, motor-generator or engine-generator are regulators (one for each welder) for adjusting the welding current to the desired value.

In cases where the mains supply voltage is 70/100 volts A.C. or 69/100 volts D.C., the regulator alone is required to enable welding to be carried out direct from the mains. For most work there is little to choose between alternating and direct current, except that A.C. gives a smoother arc when very high currents are used, and D.C. is essential when welding certain non-ferrous metals. The extension of the grid system throughout the country is making A.C. supplies available in most areas, and A.C. transformer equipment is usually preferred because it is low in first cost and requires very little maintenance.

For some types of electrodes, particularly for welding high-alloy steel and non-ferrous metals, D.C. welding supply is essential. To obtain a D.C. supply from A.C. mains either an A.C./D.C. motor-generator set or rectifying equipment is necessary. For welding very thin material it is advisable to use a small set giving stepless regulation of welding current from 10 to 150 amps. Heavy work may require 600 amps, but for general work a current range up to 300 amps is adequate.

A.C. EQUIPMENT

Equipment for one welder consists of a transformer and regulator built into a single unit. The set is connected to one phase of the A.C. supply. Two-operator sets built into a single unit will supply 300 amps for two welders, or 600 amps for one welder when required. Larger installations comprise a three-phase transformer with separate regulators, the total number of welders supplied being three, six or twelve. The transformer is connected to all three phases of a three-phase supply, and is wound in such a way as to balance as nearly as possible the load on each line irrespective of the number of welders working at any particular moment.

The standard regulator controls current up to 300 amps and is used for electrodes from 16 S.W.G. up to $\frac{1}{4}$-in. diameter, i.e. for welding steel from 20-gauge up to 1-in. thickness or even more. For regular production work on steel over $\frac{1}{2}$ in. thick, economy is obtained by using $\frac{5}{16}$-in. and $\frac{3}{8}$-in. electrodes requiring up to 600 amps: this current is obtained from a larger welding set or from two 300-amp sets connected in parallel.

Fig. 34 shows the wiring of a typical portable welding set. It is, however, intended only to illustrate the general principles involved and should not be used in place of detailed instructions.

The welding set should be connected to the mains via a

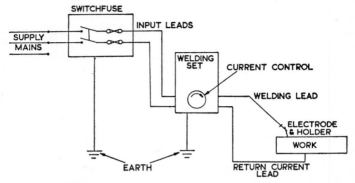

Fig. 34. An arc welding circuit diagram. The set should be connected to a single-phase
supply or two lines of a three-phase supply.

switch-fuse, and the switch, set and work (or bench) should
be earthed. The welding leads are heavy cables with tough
rubber insulation. One makes a direct connection between
the set and the work to be welded—or an iron (or steel)
bench if the work is to be carried out on the bench—and
the other lead connects the electrode holder to the welding
set.

It is important to be familiar with the method of adjusting
the current regulator, and with the operation of the mains
switch. For small work it is necessary to have an iron (or
steel) topped bench permanently connected to the return
lead of the welding set.

D.C. Mains Supply

D.C. mains supply above 100 volts is reduced to welding
voltage by means of a motor-generator set. In this case a
D.C. motor drives a D.C. welding current generator.

Electricity supply undertakings throughout the country
are working towards the standardisation of all public

supplies as A.C., and therefore the local supply undertaking should be consulted before D.C. equipment is installed.

ENGINE-DRIVEN SETS

Where the welding current is to be generated on the spot, or for repair work on site, it is customary to use a D.C. generator driven by a petrol or oil engine, the whole forming a self-contained portable unit.

WELDING ACCESSORIES

In addition to the welding set, cables and electrode holder, the welder will also require the following accessories:

(1) Non-conducting hand screen and/or head screen fitted with protective coloured glass.

(2) Leather gauntlet gloves for protection of hands and wrists, and (optional) a leather apron.

(3) Chipping hammer ⎱ For removing slag and clean-
(4) Wire brush ⎰ ing the work.

(5) Chipping goggles with clear glass for eye protection when chipping slag.

The protective glass fitted in the welding screen absorbs the ultra-violet and infra-red rays emitted by the arc, both of which are very harmful to the eyes. The glass should not only be of the right density to secure good vision of the arc, but also should be effective in cutting off the harmful rays. (See British Standard No. 679:1947.) *Never look at the arc except through the proper protective glass.*

ELECTRODES

An electrode consists of a metal core wire with an insulating covering. The welding operation depends largely

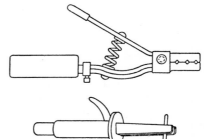

Fig. 35. Two types of electrode holders.

for its success on the covering, which is a complicated metallurgical product.

The functions of the covering are as follows:

(1) To stabilise the arc and enable A.C. to be used.

(2) To flux away impurities present on the surface of the material being welded.

(3) To form a slag over the weld. The slag (*a*) protects the molten metal from contamination by the air, (*b*) reduces the rate of cooling of the weld, and (*c*) smooths out the wave formation on the surface of the weld.

(4) To compensate for losses of alloying constituents, some of which are more volatile or more subject to oxidation than others.

(5) To speed up the process by increasing the melting rate.

From this it will be seen that no attempt should be made to use electrodes from which the covering has been wholly or partially removed. The efficiency of the electrode is impaired if the covering is allowed to become damp, and thus if the electrodes become damp they should be dried before use by placing them in a warm cabinet for a few hours.

Bare electrodes (i.e. without a covering) are sometimes used but, for the reasons given above, these give poor results in comparison with the coated types.

The 'Shielded Arc'

Mention was made earlier of the use of a 'blanket' of inert argon gas to prevent contamination of the molten weld metal by oxygen from the atmosphere. A similar effect can be obtained in metal arc welding by using special electrodes having a heavy coating that gives off large quantities of a gas which envelopes and completely shields the weld area from the atmosphere (*Fig. 36*). Known as the 'shielded arc', this technique gives welds of exceptionally high strength and quality.

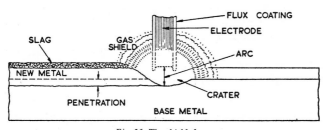

Fig. 36. The shielded arc.

Specifying Welding Procedure

When consulting handbooks it will be found that the procedure for making welds is often denoted by two figures, thus: 6/11, ¼/7, etc. For example, if the procedure for making a fillet with $\frac{1}{4}$-in. legs is given as '6/11', this means that the speed of welding and the general technique employed must be such as to use up one entire 6-gauge electrode in making a $\frac{1}{4}$-in. fillet weld of 11 in. length. In the case of '$\frac{1}{4}$/7' procedure, a $\frac{1}{4}$-in. diameter electrode must be completely deposited in a weld length of 7 in.

CUTTING WITH THE ARC

It is possible to use the arc for cutting purposes, but this should only be done if gas cutting equipment is not available. In effect, the operation consists of melting away the steel so that a slot is formed. The width of the cut is about twice the diameter of the electrode, and the electrode melts away rapidly. The process is neither neat nor economical, but is very useful in an emergency for cutting mild steel. It can also be employed for cutting cast iron, stainless steel and corroded wrought iron, all of which are difficult to cut with the oxygen blowpipe.

To cut, use an 8, 6 or 4 S.W.G. electrode and set the current to twice the maximum welding current, i.e. 300, 400 or 500 amps respectively. When about half of the electrode has been consumed put the remainder aside to cool for use again later.

With the plate horizontal and the electrode at about 45° hold a fairly long arc and move the tip of the electrode up and down the edge of the plate. As the metal melts, 'brush' it downwards with the arc. Feed the electrode into the slot that is formed and continue working the tip of the electrode up and down to melt the plate and assist the molten metal to run away downwards.

CHAPTER IX

METALLIC ARC WELDING PROCEDURE

STRIKING THE ARC

To strike an arc the electrode should be directed at an angle of 60° to the horizontal (see *Fig. 37*). With the welding screen placed in front of the eyes, the tip of the electrode is touched on to the plate with a movement similar to that for striking a match.

Contact with the plate closes the electric circuit, and current flows. On drawing the tip of the electrode a little away from the plate, the current continues to flow across the gap, forming an electric arc, which is the source of welding heat. The gap may be drawn out to an inch or more before the arc breaks, but in order to control the deposition of electrode material it must be kept short.

Learners often experience difficulty with the electrode 'sticking' to the work. When this occurs the holder should

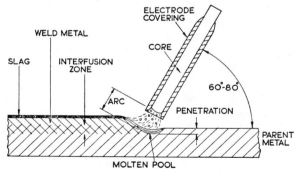

Fig. 37. The theory of metal-arc welding.

be given a sharp twist to free the electrode. If the electrode is not freed immediately, pull out the switch.

Once the arc has been struck, the electrode will melt, requiring a downward movement of the electrode holder to maintain the arc at the correct length. The tip of the electrode should be approximately $\frac{1}{8}$ in. from the molten pool, and the arc must be watched closely at all times to keep it the right length. It will be found that the downward movement of the electrode holder required to maintain the arc will come quite naturally if the arc is closely watched all the time.

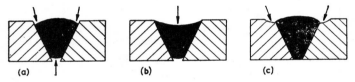

Fig. 38. Common weld faults. Key: (a) insufficient fusion, (b) not enough filler metal and (c) undercutting.

The tip of the electrode must be moved along the plate in order to avoid getting a large pool of molten metal in one place. A continuous light touch on the plate gives the correct length of arc for making small runs. On the other hand, pressure on the electrode or contact with the molten pool will cause the arc to cease and the electrode to stick. When making a large run the molten pool catches up with the tip of the electrode, which must therefore be raised slightly to maintain the arc. Too long an arc makes a fluttering noise and is to be avoided. After completion of the run remove the slag with the chipping hammer and examine the deposited metal: the slag will come away more easily when cold.

A run made with a slow movement of the electrode gives a thicker and shorter weld than one made by drawing the electrode rapidly, and it is necessary to practise making runs until the length of the run of metal per electrode can be varied at will. Any variation in the width or thickness of individual runs is due to irregular movement of the arm.

Alteration of welding current values above or below the recommended figures will have a definite effect on the behaviour of the electrode, and also on the appearance of the finished run. If the welding current is too low, the metal tends to pile up, and the weld surface will be lumpy and irregular in width. On the other hand, if excessive current is used, a flat deposit will result, with undue spatter and wastage of the electrode.

The correct length of arc is important. If it is unduly lengthened the weld metal is deposited, not in a steady stream of small particles, but in large globules which are accompanied by a series of explosions causing spatter and wastage of metal; the rate of deposition is retarded, and the weld is irregular and of poor appearance.

Each time the arc is broken, either by accidental interruption or for the purpose of continuing with a new electrode, a crater is formed at the finish of the run. This crater is usually inclined at an angle to the top surface of the run and if the new run commences at the feet of the incline a hollow depression will be left: if started too high on the incline an unsightly lump will be produced. Thus immediately the arc is struck the tip of the electrode should be moved to a point just below the highest point of the crater and welding resumed in the normal way.

After a little practice the welder will readily distinguish the brighter-looking slag from the darker weld metal, and observe their respective behaviour in the molten state. He will notice that the slag floats on top of the weld metal, and always tends to flow away from the electrode tip and to pile itself on top of the weld deposit: also, that the slag separates easily from the weld metal and does not intermingle with it. All good electrodes normally act automatically in this respect when simple flat position welding is carried out. These conditions should be carefully studied in order to be able to control both metal and slag when more difficult welds are attempted.

GENERAL HINTS

The recommended current range for each type of electrode is printed on the packet, and should be adhered to wherever possible. However, variations within the recommended current range are sometimes necessary to meet special conditions, and a guide to these is given in the Table below.

Welding Position	Plate Thickness (Compared with diam. of electrode)		
	Thin	Medium	Thick
Horizontal (Fillets, etc.) Downhand (Butts and tilted fillets)	*Current:* Low Medium	*Current:* Medium High	*Current:* High High
Overhead	Low	Medium	Medium
Vertical Down	Low	Medium	Medium
Vertical Up	—	Very Low	Low
Inclined	—	Very Low	Low

In addition, make slight adjustments for size of run.
Long thin runs require higher currents.
Short thick runs require lower currents.

A phenomenon known as 'arc blow' sometimes occurs when using direct current. The arc becomes wild and uncontrollable due to the magnetic effect of the current flowing in the job being welded. When using D.C., this fault can usually be cured by altering the position of the clamp which holds the return lead to the work in order to provide a different path through the work for the current. Another solution is to change the polarity of the electrode and work connection, thus reversing the direction of current flow. A third solution is, if possible, to wind the electrode holder cable two or three times around the work. Arc blow does not occur when using A.C., and for this reason A.C. is preferred for high welding currents.

Never take up slack in a welding cable by coiling it around iron or steel, as this forms a reactance which cuts down the current available. The resistance of the cable causes current loss, and for this reason it is advisable to work as near the transformer as possible, so that the long leads can be on the high tension side of the transformer, where the current is lower. In cases where long welding leads are used it may be necessary to set the regulator one or two stops higher than for welding with short leads.

It is important to ensure that the return connection from the work to the set is at least as good as the electrode holder connection. In the case of site welding it is undesirable for the current to find its way back to the welding set via a partly completed building or ship. Instead, the return cable should be clamped as close to the welding set as possible, and as the structure progresses the welder should move the return cable so as to keep it as short as possible.

REINFORCING OR BUILDING-UP

The following is the procedure for building-up a surface by laying parallel runs side by side to form added metal of uniform thickness. *It is important that the runs partially penetrate each other.* After laying the first run, remove the slag by means of the chipping hammer and wire brush and then deposit the second run alongside it, using a side-to-side movement of the tip of the electrode so that the run overlaps the first run for about one-third of its width.

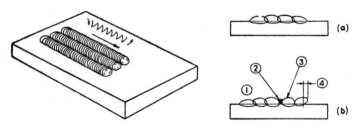

Fig. 39. Reinforcing or building-up. Common faults are shown in (b). These are (1) runs piled, (2) trapped slag, (3) runs too thick and narrow and (4) run overlaps without penetrating. A correct weld is shown at (a).

The electrode should be held at an angle of about 60°, but instead of being in-line with the direction of the travel should be turned sideways so that the tip is directed into the angle formed by the edge of the first run with the surface of the plate. The second run is built up to the level of the top of the first run without any valley or ridge between them. Also, the two deposits must be thoroughly fused over their entire length (*Fig. 39*). Common faults which arise are illustrated in *Fig. 39*: these are (1) the runs are piled on each other, (2) the runs are too thick and too narrow, (3) the runs overlap without penetration, and (4) slag is

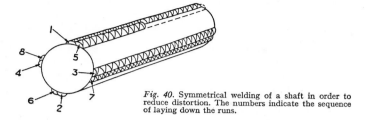

Fig. 40. Symmetrical welding of a shaft in order to reduce distortion. The numbers indicate the sequence of laying down the runs.

trapped between the runs, this latter fault being due to failure to remove the slag after making the preceding run.

The diagram in *Fig. 40* shows how a shaft should be reinforced in order to reduce distortion due to uneven application of the welding heat. This procedure permits each run to cool slightly before the adjacent run is laid beside it, thus minimising the heat at any one place.

Corner Joints

The first run is deposited in the bottom of the Vee formed between the edges and should be flat, of even thickness, and should show through the underside of the joint uniformly along its length. The electrode should be held in line with the joint and at an angle of about 60° (*Fig. 41*). Care must

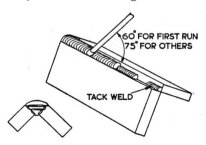

60° FOR FIRST RUN
75° FOR OTHERS

TACK WELD

Fig. 41. Making a corner weld in mild steel. The correct section is shown on the left.

be taken to ensure that the metal is deposited equally on each plate and not more on one edge than on the other. After completion of the first run, clean the first layer thoroughly.

The second layer is made by giving a slight lateral movement to the tip of the electrode, and travelling at a sufficient speed to fuse the plate edges and to fill the Vee about two-thirds of the way up. After removal of the slag a further similar run should be made. In most cases the third run will be sufficient to complete the joint. Now turn the work over and make a light sealing run inside the corner. The current for this run should be higher than for the first run because it has to penetrate all the irregularities in the underside of the first run. The size of this run must be adjusted to make the full throat thickness of the completed weld equal to the plate thickness (*Fig. 41*).

Very little lateral movement of the electrode is necessary, and if a wide run is involved it is better to use a large electrode than to attempt to weave widely with a small-gauge electrode because the latter is liable to cause slag inclusions or undercut.

FILLET WELDS

If possible, when making fillet welds it is advisable to tilt the joint so that the weld is made in a flat position, and thus equal fusion into each plate is assisted by gravity. In most respects this type of weld is similar to a corner weld, except that, because there is no gap at the root, the current is higher in order to obtain good penetration.

The plates should first be tack welded. The electrode should bisect the angle formed by the plates, and should be held at an angle of 70° to the direction of travel. The first run should pass over the tack welds (previously deslagged), slightly increasing the speed whilst doing so. The production of a neat and sound fillet weld is largely a matter of experience because only by experience is it possible to learn how fast to move the electrode, and how to gauge the size of the leg being made as welding proceeds.

Particular attention must be paid to (1) making the two legs of the fillet equal, (2) keeping the surface of the weld flat, (3) avoiding undercutting the plates, and (4) in the case of a lap weld, avoiding melting down the corner. All of these points are solved by keeping a short arc and by holding the electrode at the correct angle.

Butt Welds

When two plates lying in the same plane are to be joined edge-to-edge, the edges are usually bevelled to give a 60° Vee (*Fig. 42*). First tack the plates together, leaving a small root gap, and then put down the first run. The degree of penetration is very sensitive to small variations in root gap, but the penetration may be kept consistent by using a current to suit the root gap. As welding proceeds the plates may tend to draw together, thus reducing the root gap, and for this reason the tack welds must be strong enough to prevent any appreciable closing of the gap.

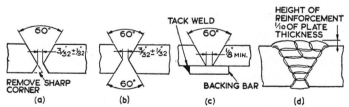

Fig. 42. Flat butt welds in mild steel. Key: (a) single-vee preparation, (b) double-vee preparation, (c) preparation for welding from one side only, and (d) method of reinforcing a large weld.

The number of runs required will depend upon the thickness of the plate, but each run must be thoroughly deslagged and cleaned before laying down the next. In general, the thickness of any run should not greatly exceed $\frac{1}{8}$ in., otherwise there is a chance of porosity and slag inclusions occurring. Obviously a very thick run will have a correspondingly thick layer of slag, and the slag will ultimately run down and around the electrode, making further welding difficult.

It is customary to deposit in the Vee a run whose width does not exceed $2\frac{1}{2}$ times the diameter of the electrode. However, when welding a large Vee with small electrodes, is it advisable to adopt the procedure shown in *Fig. 42*d, filling in the width with two or more runs side by side. In all butt joints the weld metal must be built up just above the level of the plate, the extra height being 10 per cent of the plate thickness or $\frac{1}{8}$ in., whichever is less.

The back of the butt weld must be completed by a small sealing run. If the penetration of the first run has been inadequate or uneven it will be necessary to chip the back out with a round-nose chisel before laying down the sealing run. This work will not be necessary if the first run penetrates evenly to the underside, and thus it is important to set up the plates with the correct root gap, and to use just enough current for the first run. The size of electrode for the sealing run is not important, but should be kept to the smallest size that will make a neat and smooth run.

Plates above $\frac{3}{4}$-in. thickness nearly always require double-Vee preparation, whilst plates under $\frac{1}{2}$-in. thickness usually have a single Vee. Between these two thicknesses either type may be used. The saving in weld metal achieved by the use of the double Vee may be gauged from the fact that it requires only half the weld metal that would be required if a single Vee were made in the same plate thickness. In order to equalise the contractional strains, and thus preserve the alignment of the plates, it is advisable, if possible, to turn the job over after each run. With large and heavy work it may be advisable to make two runs on each side before turning over.

It often happens that the work cannot be turned over or the joint is accessible from one side only, and in such cases it is necessary to use a backing strip. The plates are bevelled to a sharp edge, and a root gap of at least ⅛ in. must be provided (*Fig. 42c*). The first run fuses the plates and also fuses into the backing strip, this making a smooth sound weld at the bottom of the Vee. The first run is made with a high current, as there is no danger of excessive penetration. The remaining runs are made in a similar manner to those for any other Vee welds. The backing strip should be tack welded to one plate before bringing the plates together. After completion of welding it is, of course, removed.

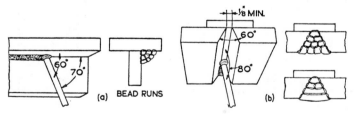

Fig. 43. Overhead (a) fillet weld and (b) butt weld.

OVERHEAD WELDING

Provided that small runs are made, overhead welding (*Fig. 43*) is not difficult. However, a large joint requires a great number of runs and therefore is slow and tedious, and for this reason overhead welding should be avoided wherever possible. Whilst welding is proceeding satisfactorily, the operation is comparatively simple, but once a slag hole or hanging drop of metal is formed it is difficult to put right. In such cases the only solution is to stop welding, chip out the bad part and start again. Protection against falling sparks is essential, and the head screen, leather apron and gauntlet gloves should always be worn.

VERTICAL WELDING

There are two methods of vertical welding, i.e. upwards and downwards (*Fig. 44*). The characteristics of each are (1) upwards—current used is low, the penetration is good, a large weld can be made in one run, and the run is slightly convex and of irregular surface: (2) downwards—current used is medium, penetration is poor, and each run is small,

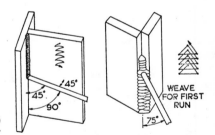

Fig. 44. Welding vertically (left) downwards and (right) upwards.

concave and smooth. The downwards method is used for making welds on thin material, for making sealing runs on heavier material, and sometimes as a 'wash run' on the outside of a large upwards weld when a neat appearance and smooth finish are particularly desired.

VERTICAL DOWNWARDS WELDING

With a medium current strike an arc somewhere near the top of the joint, bring the tip of the electrode into the corner at the top and commence a weave, as shown in *Fig. 44* (left). The electrode must be kept continually on the move, not fast, but without stopping. If there is a pause a hot spot will be produced and molten metal will drop down. The slag will stay above the electrode until a quantity has collected, when it will drop down in front of the electrode. When it does this, help it down right out of the way by drawing a long arc and making a movement as though brushing it down with the arc. As soon as it is clear bring the electrode back into the welding position, with a short arc.

UPWARDS WELDING

All strength joints in vertical plates $\frac{3}{8}$ in. thick or more are welded upwards. With a low current start in the corner near the bottom. After a slight pause move downwards to the left. After another pause move to the other plate. Pause here and then move up into the corner again. The correct weave is shown in *Fig. 44* (right). The object is to keep the top surface of the weld sloping down away from the corner so that the slag runs away and does not become trapped.

Clean off the slag and make one more run to complete the weld. Keep the weld face sloping down away from the first run. There will now be two top corners, with a pause to be made in each, the method being otherwise the same as that used for the first run. The run length will be 2 to 3 in.

With bigger runs special care must be taken to build up in the corner first and keep the weld face sloping down away from the corner.

SHEET METAL

There are two quite different methods for welding sheet metal. One is to use an electrode comparable to the sheet thickness—e.g. 16 S.W.G. electrode for 18 S.W.G. sheet, 14 S.W.G. electrode for 16 S.W.G. sheet, etc.—welding in the same way as for thicker material.

The other method is to use much larger electrodes which are held in light contact with the joint and travelled rapidly to make runs up to 36 in. long per electrode. This method is known as 'touch welding' and it enables very high welding speeds to be attained. A good fit-up is essential for touch welding with large electrodes. This method is therefore employed for production work where jigs are used, whilst 'one-off' jobs and repair work are usually welded by the slower method using small electrodes.

It is important to set up *all* types of joints on 12 S.W.G. and thinner sheets without any gap. If a jig is not used it will be necessary to put down enough tack welds to hold the parts in position. The pitch of tack welds can be determined from the formula—$P = 4$ in. $+ 16$ T. (T. = plate thickness): this gives a pitch of 5 in. for 16 S.W.G. plate, which must be regarded as the maximum: often, tacks as close as 3-in. pitch are necessary, and for this reason the use of tacks should be avoided whenever possible.

CHAPTER X

TECHNIQUES FOR VARIOUS METALS

Given below is a summary of the weldability of various metals by the metallic arc process. Details regarding the current values, polarity, welding position, etc., will be found on the packets in which the electrodes are supplied. They may vary slightly from make to make, and for this reason are not given below.

MILD STEEL

Mild steel is easily welded. All the data regarding arc welding techniques given earlier in this book refer to mild steel unless specifically stated otherwise.

CARBON STEELS

Steels with a carbon content of 0.25 to 0.3 per cent can be welded without preheating, provided that large runs are made. For welding with ferritic electrodes, steels having a carbon content of 0.3 to 0.5 per cent should be preheated to 100° to 350° C., according to the carbon content. When it is not practicable to preheat they may be welded with austenitic electrodes.

Cracking in the weld is usually due to carbon 'pick-up', and this can largely be prevented by coating the surfaces with a layer of weld metal before joining them together. This layer picks up some carbon, but as it is not highly stressed on cooling it does not usually crack. The joining run should be made while the job is still warm from the deposition of the above 'buttering' runs. When welding carbon steel to mild steel, it is not necessary to 'butter' the mild steel.

STEEL CASTINGS

All sand and porous metal must be removed before applying weld metal. If a crack in a thin part of the casting has been caused by uneven cooling or faulty design of the casting, it is liable to crack again after welding. Remember that the weld will shrink, and thus use a low current in order to keep the temperature low.

Contractional stresses in castings that have not been normalised must be reduced by careful welding. Normalised mild steel castings may be welded without any special precautions. Medium-carbon castings must be preheated: if they have not been normalised, special care is necessary.

Normalising after welding is beneficial to both the casting and weld metal, provided that no cracks have appeared during welding. Cracked metal cannot be repaired by heat treatment: it must be chipped out and welded.

MANGANESE STEEL

Manganese steel work-hardens rapidly, and therefore the degree of structure change must be kept to the minimum by keeping the temperature as low as possible. This is done by using a low current and allowing time to cool between each run. The current values recommended are about 25 per cent lower than for the equivalent size of mild steel electrode. In no case should the maximum values quoted on the electrode carton be exceeded.

Special electrodes depositing an austenitic chrome-nickel alloy are used for strength welding manganese steel and for welding mild steel to manganese steel. In the latter case, trouble may be caused by dilution of the electrode alloy by pick-up of mild steel. To prevent this, use the lowest possible current and make a large run. In some cases it may be necessary to 'butter' the surface of the mild steel with a layer of weld metal before making a strength weld.

Manganese steel reinforcements should be built up in small narrow runs. To prevent cracking, the work must be kept as cool as possible, and thus welding should be proceeded with slowly, allowing time to cool between each run. When making strength welds it is often advisable to make a large first run using a low current.

STAINLESS STEEL

The 18/8 steels are easily welded with electrodes specially developed for the purpose. These contain columbium, and their corrosion-resisting properties are equal in every respect to columbium-bearing stainless steel. The electrodes are supplied in shorter lengths than usual in order to prevent overheating during welding. Stainless steel is liable to distort more than other metals, and should always be clamped firmly or tack welded at close pitch.

For butt welding sheet up to 8 S.W.G. leave a gap equal to the thickness of the sheet. To prevent the gap closing, tack welds should be made, at a pitch of 2 in. for 22 S.W.G. sheets, this increasing to 6-in pitch for 8 S.W.G. sheets. The tacks should achieve full penetration and should have a flat surface so that they can be welded over without spoiling the uniformity of the final run. Use a higher current for tack welding. Do not attempt to penetrate through a close butt joint in thin sheet by using a high current, because a hole will result instead of a weld. It is *essential* to set up butt joints with the correct gap.

For butt welds in plate thicker than 8 S.W.G. the edges should be bevelled to give a 60° Vee, and a $\frac{1}{8}$-in. gap at the root. Corner welds and fillet welds do not present any difficulty. When welding, it is advisable to make narrow runs and to hold a short arc to prevent loss by volatilisation of the alloying constituents.

Most stainless steel electrodes can be used for depositing a stainless steel on other steels. Where the base metal contains above 0.2 per cent carbon, two layers of weld deposit are necessary to obtain full corrosion-resisting properties.

When welding stainless steel to mild steel the use of a mild steel type of electrode is quite satisfactory, but the technically sound procedure is to employ a highly alloyed austenitic electrode of the type designed specially for welding non-austenitic steels. This gives a truly austenitic deposit even when used on mild steel.

Clad Steels

These usually consist of a thin sheet of stainless steel securely bonded to a thicker backing of mild steel. The special stainless steel electrodes are used for the stainless steel side, and mild steel type electrodes for the mild steel side. It is important to ensure that the stainless steel weld on the clad side is not contaminated by pick-up of mild steel. This applies also in cases where nickel or other cladding metals are used.

Heat Resisting Steels

The method of welding these steels is the same as for stainless steel, i.e. the runs should be narrow and the arc should be short in order to prevent loss of alloying elements by volatilisation. The expansion of these steels is 50 per cent greater than that of mild steel, and therefore adequate clamping and tack welding are required to prevent distortion.

The valves fitted to the engines of private cars and light lorries are usually of chrome-silicon composition. These can be reinforced with the type of electrode used for welding stainless steel. Bad pitting or oxidation of the face must be ground off prior to welding.

HARD SURFACING

The electrodes for hard surfacing consist of special alloy steels, and for this reason must always be used with a low-to-medium current, and a short arc, so as to prevent loss of alloying materials in the arc.

When hard surfacing mild steel it is advisable to apply at least two layers of weld metal because the first layer is diluted by pick-up from the plate and does not have full wear-resisting properties. To make allowance for wear, three layers are generally necessary, but it is not advisable to attempt to make more than three layers because such a mass of weld metal may crack on deposition or if subsequently subjected to severe shock.

If a thick reinforcement is required on high tensile steels containing appreciable quantities of nickel, chromium and molybdenum, particularly those with a carbon content above 0.25 per cent., it is advisable to make the first layer with mild steel electrodes, followed by two layers with hard surfacing electrodes. It is not necessary to put down this layer of mild steel when the total thickness of reinforcement does not exceed two layers.

CAST IRON

A very low current must be used when welding cast iron in order to keep stresses and penetration to the minimum. Two types of electrodes are available, i.e. ferrous and non-ferrous. The former is used for welds requiring maximum possible strength, whilst the latter gives a slightly softer deposit which is particularly suitable for machining.

Welding is liable to produce a hard zone just away from the weld, and this may be avoided by preheating to about 300° C. Preheating also reduces contraction stresses, and thus reduces chances of the casting cracking. Preheating is a safety precaution and is not essential except for castings of complicated shape, or where the presence of a hard zone is not permissible. Make small runs, not more than 3 in. long at a time, and allow time between each run for the heat to become evenly distributed throughout the casting.

Ferrous electrodes are generally used for strength welding. If it is possible to preheat the casting and to cool it very slowly after welding, it is advisable to do so, but many strength weld repairs can be effected without preheating. The nature of the metal, the type of fracture, the stresses imposed on the casting and the best way to apply heat to avoid the formation of other cracks must all be carefully considered before welding is attempted. In general, castings should be either preheated to a fairly high temperature (above 250° C., or even red hot) or kept as cool as possible during welding. To keep the casting cool use 10 or 12 S.W.G. electrodes and make sure it is not more than hand hot before laying each run. Bronze welding may be used for thin castings (under $\frac{1}{4}$ in.) and in cases where peening is necessary. Corroded areas, rust, scale, grease and dirt *must* always be removed before welding.

Where there is no objection to a reinforcement, no preparation is used: a Vee is formed by building up weld metal on each side of the fracture to a height equal to one-third the thickness of the iron. If a flush finish is required, the casting is Vee'd to a depth totalling one-third of its thickness. In all cases, the finished job must be placed on wood or dry concrete and allowed to cool slowly, away from draughts.

When a large space is to be filled, steel studs are screwed into the casting. They are arranged in staggered rows, and the holes are drilled and tapped to different depths to spread the contractional pull over the greatest possible area. The studs should project for a distance equal to about one-half or three-quarters of their diameter. A small run of ferrous weld metal is first put around each stud, and the weld then built up on the protrusions so formed.

Bronze Welding Cast Iron

It is essential to prepare the surface by grinding down to clean metal. Small runs are made, using the current recommended by the electrode manufacturer. In some instances the top of the first run may be porous, in which case the porous metal should be filed off: the subsequent runs will be solid. In order to prevent contraction stress, each run may be peened (while still hot) by light blows with a small hammer.

Malleable Iron

To avoid spoiling the properties of this metal, welding must be on the surface only and must be carried out with the lowest possible current so as to avoid thermal disturbance of the metal below the decarburised skin. Use ferrous electrodes of the type employed for cast iron: use the smallest size and the lowest current. Alternatively, tin-copper bronze electrodes may be employed: as bronze melts at a lower temperature than iron or steel the work is kept cooler by this method. With either type of electrode keep the work cool by welding only a short distance at a time, *but do not quench in water*. When a reinforcement has been deposited, a joint may be made or further layers built up with larger electrodes, but always using minimum current. *On no account should any preparation such as bevelling be employed.* Malleable iron can be joined to mild steel, using either of the electrodes mentioned above.

ALUMINIUM

Aluminium is weldable, but there is difficulty in fluxing the highly refractory oxide. For this reason it is usually gas-welded. It can be arc-welded, but there is much room for improvement in electrodes before the arc-welding of aluminium becomes comparable to the arc-welding of steel.

MAGNESIUM

This metal can be welded by the atomic-hydrogen process, by the argon-arc process, or by the oxy-acetylene, but not at present by the metallic-arc process.

NICKEL

Nickel is readily weldable, using nickel electrodes. The need for this usually only arises when welding clad steels.

ZINC

Because of its low temperature of volatilisation, zinc is usually gas welded.

MONEL METAL

Monel metal is a 70/30 nickel-copper alloy with remarkable corrosion-resisting properties and considerable strength